Imagine—writing made with blood tattooed in books, the libraries which the *conquistadores* burned. In *Pura Neta*, Benjamin Bac Sierra gives us such a poetic work for our time.

—Maxine Hong Kingston, author of *The Woman Warrior*

Pura Neta is uniquely Benjamin Bac Sierra. His experiences in the Bay Area's *barrio* streets, in the Gulf War, and as a highly-educated activist for justice in our communities intertwine with a poet's pen, a storyteller's heart, and the barrio's unflinching eyes. You will want to read this more than once to revel in the heavily mined depths laden with secrets and treasures.

—Luis J. Rodriguez, author of *Always Running, La Vida Loca*

Pura Neta is poetry. It is a chorus singing out its history. A poignant elegy for comrades and a city consumed by gentrification, racism, police brutality. An invigorating cry of revolution. Benjamin Bac Sierra, the Bard of the Mission, bears witness to a changing San Francisco and affirms that real power lies with people "creating concoctions of craziness and putting it all into action"!

—Shawna Yang Ryan, American Book Award Winner, author of *Green Island*

Pura Neta—Blood and fire poems, tears; the absurdity of the rose given as an offering on an altar of wisdom that Ben Bac Sierra presents through voices that inhabit the songs of the soul of Frisco, the soul of our community, a portal into our deepest thoughts, overcoming shame, claiming and singing out who we are, from the shoulder, from the chest, and finally from the throat, flaming with flowers that refuse to be massacred, that continue to color the mountains that make up our dreams. Ben Bac Sierra honors the voices that haunt, love, and finally, guide us towards ov ʰ— perfection—which is a poem of *Pura Neta*.

—Tony R ʹsidence, ₋erstrike

Ben Bac Sierra's *Pura Neta* breathes the living and the dead mixing it up on the barrio streets, with authentic dialogue, sharply drawn characters, and an effortless combination of poetry and prose, compelling you to keep reading. The real deal of *La Misión*, tough love in every sentence. Ben transports us to a place only he can describe, where: "Every day is the apocalypse."

—Alejandro Murguía, San Francisco Poet Lauréate Eméritas

As I beheld the stark images and pristine lyricism found in *Pura Neta*, it became clear that the words found between its pages had been penned by someone who had truly been about that life. Only someone who had lived it could have painted the characters with such 3-D precision. Taking its readers on a spiritual quest that ignores the conventions of time, *Pura Neta* is gutter, gangsta, and mystical all at the same time. In his arms, with such tenderness and respect, Bac Sierra cradles the souls and streets of the San Francisco Mission, embracing both the courage and fragility of the place he loves and its people. Like the late James Baldwin, Benjamin Bac Sierra is a witness who testifies with his pen. *Pura Neta* is his triumph and ours.

—Harry Louis Williams, II aka O.G. Rev,
author of *Straight Outta East Oakland*

One of Benjamin Bac Sierra's characters, Cartoon, said it best, 'A good writer is supposed to hit you on the head and the reader is supposed to say thank you for the lump.' His characters' voices get into your head and stick. Bac Sierra's writing makes you see the world through someone else's eyes and changes you for the better. *Pura Neta*. This is the very essence of literature.

—Karl Marlantes, author *Matterhorn: A Novel of the Vietnam War*

PURA NETA

BENJAMIN BAC SIERRA

Pochino Press
Oakland, CA

Library of Congress Control Number: 2020944866
ISBN: 978-0-9988758-3-5

Cover art contributors — Artist: Matteo Leon-Valencia, Model: Angelina McCann, Photographer: Oscar King Studio, Car owner: Ruby "Xingona" Ramirez.

Book design by Xiomara Castro

Neta

NOTE TO THE READER

Apostrophes: In order to approximate certain words without the burden of excessive punctuation, which can distract the reader, the author sometimes intentionally omitted apostrophes so that it could be more representative of colloquial language. For example, in standard English "isn't" requires an apostrophe to separate "is" and "not", but "aint" aint even a standard word, so there is actually no logical reason to separate "ai" from "not." "Aint" seems to offer some type of illusion that "ain't" is formal in some way, when it is not.

Quotation marks: Since this novel is written in what may be an unprecedented style (one that integrates both stanza style poetry and orthodox prose that advance the story plot), a brief explanation of how quotation marks are used may be necessary. In the novel if the speaker is speaking or thinking to himself, no quotation marks are used bordering the poems. If, however, the speaker is dialoguing using stanza style poems, quotation marks are used as boundaries of the speaker's speech.

Background:*Pura Neta* stands on its own. It stands on its roots. To learn more about *Pura Neta*'s roots and references, please read Santo, Lobo, Toro, Maricela, and Cartoon's stories in *Barrio Bushido*.

TABLE OF CONTENTS

CHAPTER ONE — FINDING BALANCE

"Homeboy," Lobo had said to Lil Cartoon back in 1992, "I'm gonna be direct. This has all been for you. Times are changing and we need real steel to deal with it. I'm in too deep, but you're still a runt, sixteen years old, just craving for the big time. Well, all right, I've chosen you cause you got qualities that I think can be transformed into other avenues of opportunity. Lil Toon?"

"Yeah?" Lil Cartoon answered sitting in a plush red wing chair in Lobo's opulent Victorian living room on the backstreets of the Mission district.

"I'm going to ask you to be brave, and show me some strength."

"Anything," Lil Cartoon responded. Lobo looked at the wall behind Lil Cartoon.

"Forget me. Forget all my bullshit or ignore it or however the fuck you got to psyche yourself out of the game, and get the fuck on. Motherfucker, we're getting kicked out anyway—accept it now or later."

"What the fuck you talkin bout, nigga. This is *mi varrio*, my fuckin hood." Lil Cartoon did not understand what Lobo was asking him to do. Lobo briefly grinned, his white teeth contrasted starkly from his dark brown skin, then he looked back at the wall—

"Go and be selfish, homeboy. Go and fuckin have your own mind, cause you can't help me or any of us any other way. Don't feel sorry for nothin or no one and don't cling to shit that is gonna stop you from getting to where you need to go, even if it's the thing or person you love most," Lobo clasped his hands together. "Let it go, young Brother. You got to be ruthless, and that means you got to be alone."

"I know what you're trying to say, Lobo, like I can't help anyone else out unless I first help myself. But I'm already down, Lo, and I aint your average bear," Lil Cartoon said.

With the bottom of his fist, Lobo thumped the arm of the chair he was sitting in.

"We already got too many average bear motherfuckers out there ready to die now," Lobo said. "Think they're bad cause they can give up the ghost. They're sellouts to the man up above—traitors to this world and this is the world we're living in. I aint asking you to die for shit. I'm asking you for something even harder. Toon—fuck everything you've ever known. I got faith that that shit will always stick to your ribs, so I aint worrying about you forgetting the *Vida Loca* life and values, but I don't want you to just walk around here like a fuckin zombie. Sheila's life has to have been for something." Lobo's guilt leaked into his voice. It was because of him that the love of his life was murdered. "I want you to sacrifice everything you've ever known, but I know in the end you'll come back to where you need to be." Putting his gold ringed fingers on Lil Cartoon's shoulder, twenty-two year old Lobo, a smooth *varrio* shot caller, scooted closer.

"Learn. Cause I've been making major paper for the past year, ever since that big lick we handled, and I realize, even with gold and platinum, I aint got shit. We aint got shit. We're fuckin laughingstocks. These motherfuckers moving in see *gente* as jokes. We're maids and housekeepers, and aint nothing wrong with bustin your ass, but there is something wrong with gettin no respect. There's somethin wrong when *putos* treat you like a boy. Cause the establishment thinks they got us all figured out. They think we're a bunch of dummies who can't even put up a fight in their world, and their world is where the big *lechuga* is at. They want to pacify us with talk of peaceful, non-aggressive bullshit and have us happy with crumbs. But, check out, outright revolution won't work; evolution is what's needed first. Toon, we need sacrifice like only a *vato* like you can give."

Lobo handed Lil Cartoon a Cuban cigar, lit it up for him, and lit one up for himself. He blew O's out into the air, while Cartoon held in his coughs. "Go get some education, young blood. I don't want to see you unless you got something positive to give me. If you hang around here, I'll put you down. No fuckin pity. You will sleep with the fishes, cause I aint gonna let you waste our potential. If I see that you do, I'll take that shit as a personal insult, and I'll choke you out my damn self, even though it would kill me." Lobo reached into his inside breast pocket then pulled out a fat envelope and handed it to Lil Cartoon.

"This money's yours. I won't baby you. Do what you gotta do. You got freedom from this day forward. You belong to no man, no gang. When you're done, you'll come back. I know it, and I'll be waiting with arms extended. We'll toast to the tests of life. Now," Lobo said rising to his feet, buttoning up his double-breasted cashmere coat, "Take Off." Two suits rushed behind Lil Cartoon.

Lil Cartoon got up trying to smile like if this was all some big joke. Two hefty *vatos* started scooting him out, and he turned around to protest. With blackjacks, they clipped Lil Cartoon in the back of the neck. He fell to the red and white Persian rug. Lobo walked to him, and Cartoon, still on the floor, stared down at his own reflection in Lobo's glossy black Stacy Adams.

"Remember," Lobo said, "We fly even when we fall."

His shoes were the last thing Lil Cartoon saw of Lobo.

Lil Cartoon was a nomad. He went to check out homies, but they walked away from him like if he were a leper. He wanted to buy a *torta*, but stores wouldn't sell him anything. It started drizzling outside, so he called up the homeboy who he thought would never let him down.

Toro.

That fool will let me kick it over there, he thought. At the phone booth, he dug in his pocket for change and pulled out a little scrap of paper that had Toro's phone number on it. He dialed the number and the phone started ringing.

"Hello," Toro said.

"What's up!?" Lil Cartoon said jumping up and down.

Toro slammed the phone in his ear. Lil Cartoon was about to call him back as if it were some kind of connection problem, but then he realized he was completely ostracized and homeless. Desperate, with nothing except memories, dust dreams and high skies, he walked to the cemetery and looked for Santo, as if Santo could help him out of this torture.

And it was the first time Lil Cartoon had visited Santo's grave. It was the first time he saw his headstone, and the stone was black marble and the fresh roses and carnations surrounding it were different rainbow colors. *Lobo must have paid for that shit cause no one else would have put up the bread just on the strength of remembrance*, Lil Cartoon thought. The lettering on the marker was gold and shiny and when he saw it, he knew what he had to do.

Santo's name and birth date were centered in the middle of the marker and above it the following golden words paved the way for Lil Cartoon to begin his journey:

This is Take Off.

After Lil Cartoon had bowed his head to read those golden words on Santo's tombstone, he knew he needed to Take Off—for what kind of idiot or genius would understand the insanity of that wisdom yet stay? The inscription was idiocy because how the hell is it being planted in a grave a Take Off? Genius, too, because compared to all the flying by any bird in the world, no other Take Off was truth.

Now, twenty years later in June of 2012, strolling once again through the streets of *La San Fran Misión*, he was no longer little; he was simply

Cartoon, a character in a make-believe story full of comedy and violence, absurdity and *amor*. He returned to the *varrio* to share with and learn from all the *locos*: Toro, Santo the Spirit, and El Lobo.

The scars were still fresh.

Cartoon had learned from all the hard knocks of the *varrio*. Lobo had kicked him out and forced him to be independent. Toro had trained him to charge. By going to Santo's grave after that conversation with Lobo, Santo's spirit had taught him to fly. In that flight, like Icarus, Cartoon had burned from flying too close to the sun. It was this burn that was the spark.

The beginning of education is
Death
All roads start with and lead to the
Inevitable
There is no secret
Which means
The only choice is
Life
Which is complicated by the reality
Our our days are numbered

"What to do with this thing called time?" Back in '92 Cartoon had contemplated this question after Lobo commanded him to leave in order to learn. He respected Lobo and Toro for their animalistic natures; he loved Santo for his holiness. The day he left the *varrio*, at the grave of his Saint, *El Santo*, his *carnal*, Cartoon had meditated:

"I look at this crazy life
As an animal and
As a thinker
Both matter
I don't guess about
Equality or priority
They live intertwined with each other

I extract my energy because that's what animals do
I think because I was both
Blessed and cursed with this mind

11

I can't ignore my duty to
Consciousness
Without feeling disgusted with myself

Vida Loca is also important
Cause nothing makes any sense
And that's ok
Better to accept and be at peace with
The craziness
Than to allow it to
Destroy you."

With only this knowledge and ten grand in the envelope that Lobo had given him, Cartoon left everything he had ever known, *La San Fran Misión*. His Red Road had been long, twenty years, yet not even the blink of an eye in the totality of eternity. It had been rough and crazy, exactly as he had wanted and expected it to be.

Now there was a debt to pay.

Cartoon did not think himself a savior or necessarily even want to go back. But there was some truth that he could not avoid, a nostalgia.

Let us not romanticize the past
The San Fran streets were death and despair
Muggings, shootings, stompings, and sinning
Singing, too, but the strongest songs were sad

Soul Oldies, the songs of suffering, rule forever

"It was nice to suffer with a good friend." Cartoon smiled wide at the modern day 2012 junkies, meth and opiate addicts, not just chiva, crack, or dustheads of the 80's and 90's. Ragged alcoholic homeless men pushed their carts in the cool early morning dawn. He had missed his *gente*. Twenty years had taught Cartoon an unconditional love for his people and this place. He looked down at the ground.

"My Solid Cement

On the brink of death

Or crushed from a hangover
I hugged this Earth
My mother Mission Earth
And she always comforted me
With her
Cold kiss

I would be in love
Inventing sublime imagination

Yeah
These streets were
Death and despair
Beautiful

The grime and graffiti
In the alleys are as
Gorgeous as the sunrise."

Cartoon sucked in the scent of *pan dulce* and *café* permeating throughout the streets. He was finally home again. Home, that place that is your headquarters, your privacy, your personality, and your soul. In some ways time had stood still. 1992 and 2012 were the same thing. The same things were happening.

Four o'clock in the dark dawn
A dusthead drives drunk
Four o'clock in the bitter bright
Sunshine afternoon
An *abuelita* hobbles hauling bags
Full of unpeeled *elote* and
Canned cranberry and *queso*

Every day
At all times
There is action
Cool colored creativity
Adorned urban alleys

Mountains of majesty
Hallowed grounds
A sanctuary for *locos* and ladies
La Misión
The womb of genius

Q-VO, Homes
Sup Blood
Silence
A mad dog stare
Welcomes you
To tar and cement
Spirit and soul
Amor
Amor
Amor
The fumes of *yesca* and
Lowrider exhaust are
Healthy for homeboys and homegirls

Legends lived
Strutted down these streets

Dukie Dave
Presente!
SFM Jeff
Presente!
Sleepy
Presente!
El Santo
Presente!
The list is long and
Always in all ways
They are
Presente!

Grinning, Cartoon stared into the faces of young Homeys and old *abuelita*s. He found himself the same as them.

"I'm a witness
You are witnesses
To dead people's
Smiles and songs
That will never be erased

Though they take my Brother's life,
And deny his given rights

Yes, the message will be heard,
As the four winds spread the word

And our spirit, they can't break,
Cause we got power to communicate.

No, they can't, no, they can't, no, they can't,
Take away our music."

Skinny Cartoon sang War's "They Can't Take Away Our Music" and bounced down the block feeling high, even though he hadn't smoked a *maton* in decades. He was laughing out loud to himself, to this crazy world, and he knew he looked like a madman and was happy. It was more than nostalgia. This place was his identity. And could it be? Could it actually have happened? Was he now an O.G., a *veterano*? If so, he knew it was not simply because of his own effort. He paid homage to those who had led the way:

"I am
Whatever I am
Because
Legends lived
I was there
Witnessed them
With my own eyes
Good and bad
Bravado and tragedy

On 30th and Mission
Puppet screeched to a stop

Pulled over and
Challenged
Santo
To a fist fight in
Broad daylight and
After Santo knocked Puppet down
Santo knelt down to help Puppet back up
So they could duke some more

In the middle of 24th and Mission
Midnight
Samoan savages
Knocked heads with
Brown bulls
Fists flying
Kicks punting
Bats bashing
Toro
Refused to leave
Even as everyone else
Scrammed
Once cop sirens squealed

For his loyalty
Toro was awarded
A broken leg and arm
A concussion

I was there
When Lobo
Shirt off
Scars strutting
Sprinted after enemies' cars
Moving vehicles
Down 22nd Street
Down with the sun and
On comes the night

Dominoes and drama
Drugs
Drive bys
Pimps
Penitentiaries
Perdition
War
Funerals

All of who they were
And what they taught me
Makes me
Wish
For a time that can never
Return

I'm much older now
Than they ever were
When all that insanity
Took place
Should know better
Shouldn't
Romanticize ruin
But
Still
I got standards
How can I forget
The stupidest
Most gorgeous
Things
I have ever known?

I live my life
Knowing that
Legends
Live
Listo."

Cartoon was ready, bounced up and down like a boxer in the ring. But he was surprised because the streets, the actual tar and cement, had both evolved and devolved. White people had moved in and were pretending the streets were fancier now. There were not as many Homeys, not as much anxiety, but the paranoia was of a different kind. You had to watch out for peach people wearing plaid *Pendle*-tons, hipsters walking around looking like old school *cholos* thinking they owned the joint. Techies who swore to the *gente* that they were the people's new saviors, but it was a lie, just like the missionaries had preached lies to *los Indios* here when they established *La Misión* back in 1776. In 2012 there was a new assault: gentrification.

The gentry believe in
The great chain of being
A medieval concept about
The hierarchical nature of
Everything:
To be is to be
God
Then
King
Then queen
Next nobles
Gentry

Peasants are
Pre-destined to be at the
Bottom of the chain

With their refined etiquette and
Elite educations,
The gentry
Invented
The law and lie of
Property

The earth was meant to evolve into
Cubicles
Partitions

Workspaces
Luxury condominiums

Wildflowers must be massacred

To be sure they are exterminated
Their roots must be plucked out
Their spirit smashed
Stripped of
Humanity
Heavenliness
The words human and heaven defined by
Kings and Queens

The wildflowers that have survived
Are lost
Scattered
Searching

They thirst for water
Believing their indigenous spirit
Does not deserve even
Love

The cruelest part of this all
Is the gentry-fuckation of spirit
That attempts to steal
Soul

Wildflowers are forced to forget
But they cannot erase
Colors
Red purple yellow orange
Dancing on the streets
Lovemaking in the backseat

The spirit can't shake away
Its natural roots

Feels something wrong
But doesn't know what it is
Can't articulate it
In the gentry's ultra-intellectual manner
So is instructed it is wrong
Searches for answers from
Teachers
Politicians
Intellectuals
In the schools
In the factories
In the abyss

It finds only
Lies and inexcusable
Justifications

Their eternal answer:

The wildflowers must be massacred

Yeah, Cartoon thought, *we must be massacred, but in a funny ass way, it's an honor that my enemies think so highly of me that they gotta kill me.* Cartoon was proud that they could not reason with or explain things to him; the gentry's only alternative was murder.

Cartoon did not mind. He had already lived ten lives, been killed one hundred times over. It was ok. Cartoon was searching for something else.

He hunted for his old mentor Toro.

How was the bull? What had he done with his time?

That crazy motherfucker should be murdered, Cartoon thought.

He looked for Toro at the old bull ring on 25th and Capp, and there he was, shirt off, showing off muscles and madness radiating off of his brown skin.

Toro was now an old warrior of 42, and like all good old warriors, he told war stories to an audience of youngsters who did not know any better than to believe him. Beefed up Toro saw lanky Cartoon, all 5 foot ten inches of him. He knew it was his old Homey Cartoon, but continued with his charge in the middle of the ring:

"This is
La Misión
Where
It's tradition
To take off your shirt and
Parade your
Bubbled scars
Green tattoos and
Famous stupidity

You chase cars
You get snapped!
You expect prison and proof
You won't ever change

Death is the only option

The art is in the funeral
Full of flowers
Ladies crying
Homeys drinking
You
Just on display
In your finest
Suit or
49ers Jersey
Knowing or
Not knowing
You made it to the goal:

It aint no sad story
This is a glad story
A bad story
What people with words would call
Uplifting
The day of reckoning
The day of dreams
My grand dreams

My soul beams

Fuck hitting homeruns
I don't know about winnin an Oscar or
Being president
I got no clue about scoo and
All the small smiles and
Firm handshakes that come with that

I got now and
This is what I call high—
What I think of when I hear of
Success
Accomplishment
Happiness

I'm free."

Toro knew what was supposed to happen next; he was supposed to get stabbed straight in the heart. You could not and should not speak such things and expect to live. Prepared, Toro maddogged the up and coming young matador's eyes, felt the youngster's fear. The Homey's hand was trembling. The knife was slipping away from his grip. Toro knew what he could and should do, and sometimes it just be's that way, Homes. Sometimes, the bull, after getting his ass kicked all day, all night long, and most of the time getting slaughtered for Sunday dinner, sometimes, the bull gets lucky. Slick-backed hair Cartoon, still the skinny kid after twenty years, was there, so today was a blessed day.

Toro dug his hooves into the dirt:

"Young matador
This is
The Price of the Fight

In the middle of this
Blood and guts battlefield
This life
We sense we are here

Without knowing what it means
We imagine many things but
Cannot erase our end

It will happen
Now."

Toro charged. His *morillo* muscles lifted like *lomas*, his horns pointed straight at the objective. The young man flew up high into the sky in his fancy green and yellow matador's make-up. His red cape went flying, then parachuted down.

Afterwards, after the audience left shocked and grumbling, Cartoon pulled Toro to the side, outside of the stadium gates, where all the hobos hunted for aluminum gold out of rusted-out rancid garbage bins.

"*Como estamos, mi carnal*, my flesh and blood?" Cartoon jumped on Toro before Toro bucked him off on his head. Cartoon shook out his brain that was spinning. He loved Toro and all that he stood and fought for.

Toro, the five foot six Mayan monster of a *Chapin*, looked down at him then helped him back up.

"Cartoon, I am grateful for this day." Toro lasered into Cartoon's big bug eyes.

"We are alive
While others are
Dead

That may not
Sound
Like a lot
But
Life
Is all
We have

Our
Breath
Is a
Blessing.

Yes, it's a blessing to see you, Brother." Toro was no longer a bull; he was a big teddy bear. These moments were seldom seen, two men being more than men together. *Amor*, that taboo concept amongst the macho. They proved they could be more than they were destined to be.

"You looked good in there, *Viejo*," Cartoon said as Toro nodded his heavy head. "Still fighting the good fight, eh?"

"Every day is a good day to die." Toro blew smoke out of his ringed nose.

"Yeah, and it is a beautiful day, huh? Look at that sun!" Cartoon tried to cheer up the fatalistic talk. Toro checked him.

"Have you learned anything on your journey, funny Cartoon?

Real macho men
Don't love the sun
They love the rain so they
Can hide their tears
Such simple pettiness
Such elaborate betrayal
For honor

While others attempt to avoid
The soaking
Macho men run into
Cold downpours
Sprint into showers
Shadowbox
In the rain."

Toro, hoping, looked up at the sunny sky.

"I guess I'm crazy but
They look so tough
So sincere
So ready for death

Nobody knows when
A man's heart is broken."

Toro bent his head. Cartoon realized that something was seriously wrong. He had been gone for too long.

"How is your heart, Toro?" With his own fist, Cartoon hit his heart hard.

"They don't know me anymore," Toro lamented and limped as they traveled the streets. "These people see me," Toro pointed at all the yuppies walking down Mission street lined by expensive cafes and white-bro bars and micro-breweries, "but they think something else.

I am a bull.

But they don't see me as that majestic animal. They see only a mad dog. To them, all of us are only mad dogs that disgust them. They clear out all the old *vatos*, the homeless Homeys, from their tents.

Tonight, I wish it would rain." Toro gazed up again at the cloudless heavens.

"Then I would remember and
Feel
The wise homeless men
I used to drink with at old
Union Square
24th Street
Rat infested
Fisherman's Wharf

Bearded, stinking good men
Good drinkers of
Cisco
Night Train
Mad Dog 20/20

Winos
We shared something in common

The streets

Sitting on cement stairs in
Broad daylight or
Pitch blackness
We talked about life and

Passed around a bottle
We didn't care about cooties
We cared about life
Independence

I left for four years
From 87-91
Went to war
Came back
And they were still there
But they were no longer the same
We were no longer the same
Time changed us

I was a bullet

They were mad
Talking to the sky
Shouting at the stars
Frustrated at their own faces

They did not remember me and
It was I who was sad to be forsaken
I envied them
Their strength for the streets

When the homeless love you
They also know
How to break your heart
You look at them and you know
That is me
That is me

Who has the right to be mad
When they yell at you?
They bark because
They know you
They remember you

I wish I could be remembered
By them
It is a miracle
To be cherished
To be shouted at by a
Good
Drunk
Crazy
Homeless man
In the middle of the street

You are special
Someone
Not forgotten."

Toro was no longer talking to Cartoon. He was talking to someone, something else. "Who's The Mad Dog, Homes?" Toro barked like a gruffy Marine Drill Instructor, straightened up, looked around at these new streets that did not want him. "Cause it aint me."

"No." Cartoon massaged Toro's solid shoulder. "You were always a straight up killer, but only cause they were trying to kill you. You weren't a rabid dog. That's why I've come back, to see you, out of respect." Cartoon knew these words were leading him to where he always needed to be, where he was destined to go from the moment he had accepted Santo's golden tombstone inscription.

"How is our Lobo?" Cartoon asked.

"You been gone. You don't know, huh?"

"Know what? Is he dead?"

"Lobo got busted a dozen years ago. *Coca*, gun smuggling, suicide missions—they gave him life, Homes. *Quilmas*, San Quentin, right across the Bay. Big Time," Toro answered.

Cartoon dropped his head. He should have realized even slick Lobo would not have made it. "I got to see him," Cartoon declared. "He was always the hotshot among us, and now he's had lots of time to think and learn, so he must be even smarter," Cartoon locked onto Toro's eyes. "You know I'm back to start some good shit, but I got to look in Lobo's face first, share our journeys together, and soak up his wolf wisdom. I'm gonna visit him at Quentin, shake some shit up."

Toro smiled, lifted his heavy head, did not seem sad anymore. "You have not come to bring peace, but a sword." He embraced Cartoon, smothered him in his strong muscles. "You and Lobo together, plotting shit, executing outstanding ideas, and this world is ours." Toro's voice turned sour. "A long time ago, we lost balance. You're here to bring it back." Toro knew that things were about to change for the *varrio*. Cartoon knew it, too. They did not know exactly what would happen, but they had planted this seed twenty years earlier, and now the tree was ready to flower, to explode.

"Before the sword, I got to pay respect to the spirit: Santo at La Raza Park Cemetery. Should have gone to see him before lookin for you, but I figured it was more important to visit the living instead of the dead."

"We are stuck in this world," Toro muttered. "Santo is not."

Cartoon agreed.

"Oh, shit!" Toro scratched his crew cut head. "That aint completely right, though, that Santo is just a spirit." Toro grinned, jumped a little.

"What you mean, Toro?" Cartoon asked.

"You really have been gone." Toro paused, coughed. "You left and never found out that our Brother Santo had gotten *La Loca* Maricela pregnant before he died. She was still in jail when she had the baby, and you were already gone. Lil Santo's twenty years old runnin around these streets. He helps paint the murals."

"Fuck you." Cartoon's mouth dropped. He did not know what else to say. The Brother Santo who had taught him to sail in the sky was still there to guide their spirits. Cartoon felt a respect and responsibility to share *amor* and hard knocks with Lil Santo, his dead mentor's son.

No matter that it had been twenty years, this was still Take Off.

CHAPTER TWO — EL SANTO, THE SPIRIT

My duty was for loved ones, so my life did not matter unless it was in their service, even though after all these years, nothing has really changed. Every day is the apocalypse.

The sun sparks a force
More powerful than
The atom bomb

Already the end begins
Yet we pretend
Night will never come

The seconds tick and
We laugh
When we should cry
For every moment past
Is a moment gone forever

The four horsemen
Do not fly from the clouds
He is your bus driver
She is your comfort
It is your dog
Your poet

They tell you every day
The truth
Yet you do not believe
Until the sun sets
Day destroyed
And you lay in bed
With nothing
But the torture of another
End

The revelation of who you really are

My bones are dust. My skin stripped off long ago. There is no such thing as my bones and skin. That is no longer me. I am in a state of perfection that I swallowed during my last bloody breath.

It was Sunday, September 15, 1991. Lobo, Toro, Cartoon, and I had just pulled our fattest lick in broad daylight Chinatown. I refused to wear a mask, and because of that, my face was plastered all over the news. Heavy hitters had given orders to Lobo. I knew. Always graceful, always cunning, Lobo sauntered into the shack and looked across the room at me. We stood there, and I can't say we were maddogging each other cause there was no fear or anger in our eyes. We just kept looking, trying to understand. I broke the silence:

"Santo's sick," I said about myself before Lobo could say anything. "He has a disease that only Lobo can cure. One antidote. Aint that right, Lobo?"

Lobo's pistol dangled in his hand. Lobo was always the smart one.

"Don't trip, Brother," I tried to console him, cause I could see he was sweating, "I have lived the life of a fool and now come to a fool's ending; I'm happy." I smiled.

"It is an honor to be
Betrayed by you
A Santo does not prove
Love
When things are easy
He proves
Love
During
Action and
Suffering

No worries."

Lobo handed the pistol to Lil Cartoon. He snatched it without even understanding that he was supposed to be my hitman. With Lil Toon I left the shack knowing exactly what I needed to do.

In order that Lobo or Cartoon would not have to murder me, his own *carnal*, and so that the Homeys would not get busted, I chopped off my own head in sacrifice. I could not allow Toro and Little Cartoon to spend years in prison and Lobo to bear the guilt of killing me or allowing me to be killed. I became a legend of what it means to be a righteous *cholo*, El Santo. In that moment of death, I learned:

Sometimes
In life
There is the
Sublime
That place where
Simultaneously
You are in the world yet
Outside of it
But that feeling is fleeting
You got it one moment
It's gone the next
The victory
The escape
The orgasm
The doubled-lined angel dust joint
The high is here when you puff
Then when you exhale
Smoke rises to clouds
Dancing
Leaving you
Searching for more

Nothing is perfect until your last breath

Top down cruising
Mad grunt lovemaking
Rain pours
Sunshine bakes
Flawlessness is folly

Be satisfied with
Now
Wherever you are
Because
Life

That thing
That *locura*
Is a never ending ordeal
There is no solution

Nothing is perfect until your last breath

Your last breath is completion
No right or wrong
No good or bad
Yet even at the end
Naively
We try to make it fine

On the day of my death
I am glad
No one pretended

Instead
Lobo recited a eulogy of
Pura Neta
He preached about what
A piece of shit I was
Not even a eulogy
Should try to touch stars

A better truth would have been if all
The Homeys would have
Plucked my face out of the casket
Shaved it all away
Tattooed into my skull
The most beautiful etchings to mask
My decay
But not even that would have worked

There is only one moment that matters

We all

Without knowing it
Search for
What
We will never understand
We wish for the worst dream
Perfection

Nothing is perfect until your last breath

In life the closest I could ever reach to perfection was love, love for my Brothers, street legend love status of being a down *vato loco*. Love, too, for Maricela, my long brown haired *Vida Loca Loca*, who showed me what it meant to hold honor. I miss her, guard her, talk with her. Even though she cannot always hear my words, she feels spirit. Life and death hold the same spirit. My Mari.

I loved only one
Vida Loca
Mi Amor

Who else was gonna put up with my bullshit?

The rest of em abandoned me
Left me shoeless in the street
Empty in mi alma
I deserved it

Maricela
My *Vida Loca* lover
Waited in darkness
A place without air
Ready to love me
To fuck me over
Because where there is love
You know there is fire
Pyromaniac
Treacherous
Insane

Loca!
She knew who she was
Didn't pretend anything different

Sinner that I am
I was willing to pay for my sins
To my high-priced hooker
My sweetheart soulmate
In high heels
Sexy baby strutting down the street
Smelling like apples and
Rotten eggs

I used to tiptoe behind her
Pinch my nose
Whisper "I love you"
Caress her ass
She would smile
Knowing I'd suffer for my
Machismo
The highest high
The lowest low
El Rey
El Payaso

La Muerte
Death
That hag
This bullshit
Aint got nothin on my girl
Mari
Who kisses life without shame or
Regrets
She was my right arm as long as I breathed
As long as I bearhugged life and accepted its
Absurdity
Yet still fought against it
She admired a black-eyed fighter who lost

Handed me a hot needle instead of a cold steak
I shot and flew
High

High, I am conscious in this other place. The more you are conscious
in life, the more you are cursed to consciousness in this other place, yet you
foolishly think this is paradise! Mari used to joke to me when I was tired,
cause when she would be high off *cracka*, hunting around on the rug for little
rocks she thought had fallen from her glass pipe. She wouldn't get tired. She
would keep me motivated: "You'll sleep when you're dead!" But here there
is no sleep, only insomnia, only consciousness.

I can't stop being amazed
It is not as nice
As you think
Amazement means
Eyes wide open
All the time

The beat does not stop
So much heart
Blood
Mud
To remain amazed

Staying conscious
Is an unnatural
Abomination

Because there is no sleep, I try to pass the time in what was love, a
mirror of consciousness without the constant bright lights flashing. With love
you can be in the dark and be in peace.

Peace: one May full-moon night back in 1991, we conceived Lil Santo.
Maricela and I were celebrating simply being alive together, both fucked
up and naked in the kitchen that smelled like Pine-Sol, drunk and high and
falling down dancing, me sucking on her skin and slobbering all over her
petite breasts, and she was giggling as my stiff dick stabbed her leg. Pushing
me away, she danced, my own private exotic dancer show on the linoleum

floor. She grabbed her long brown hair with her own perfect tan hands, and then she fluttered it all over herself and had no more face, only her thick straight hair rattling in front of what were her eyes and mouth. I studied beauty. I knew what I wanted and needed to do.

A rose should be picked when it blooms.

I realized what she deserved for killing me, for slaying my past of so much suffering; I saw what she deserved for daring me to love her. I looked away onto the table, and there was her reward, a mature brown banana that I picked up and peeled away slowly in front of her as she sashayed right there in the middle of paradise, a kitchen full of dirty dishes and blasting Salsa music. And she didn't care that I had unpeeled the banana, and that there was no more smile on my face. She just kept dancing and living right there in front of me, torturing me with her taboo love and the joy of an animal or primitive savage.

I betrayed her with a kiss. With the banana in my hand, I cherished her with slobbering kisses all over her neck and shoulders and olive breasts. My drool bathing her, she laughed. When I raised the axe-banana above her head, she smiled in delirium. She had known I was a murderer since the beginning. I would kill her and love her at the same time. I dove the banana down into her hair, and she grabbed my naked haunches. She was collapsing. I uplifted the banana again and down it smashed and splattered into her thick brown hair, and Maricela stooped over like an old woman, like a fucking witch old woman, and she was cackling so hard she couldn't breathe as she was dying from being killed by a smashed banana to her brain. I remained serious. How else could I be towards someone who enjoys her own death, who laughs uncontrollably at the moment of her own Three Stooges murder?

She was laughing, I was laughing, we were laughing as we made love on the linoleum floor, as I exploded my son into her. Then we took a shower in the dark, washed off each other's banana stains, and we made love again right there in the middle of our own paradise waterfall. Her happiness was a mercy. Of course, it was love, and of course I am bound to that more than to any other thing that ever existed, even in this other ether.

Sometimes I feel her also searching for me, and I whisper in Mari's ear, and she swats at me. I, too, hunt for fleas.

She used to laugh at me.

"I think I love you because you're so fuckin weird. And I know you're a motherfucker, but not like these clichés around here. With you I don't give a fuck, got no shame about being a ho, cause that aint nothin compared to the nut you are." She would smack her chewing gum between her lips.

"*Mi amor*, one day you're gonna miss my lovin," I said.

"There's always another nigga waitin in the shadows." She got defensive, too hard for her own good.

"True, true, but we know what we have, once in a lifetime love, so I swear

One day
One night
Panicked
In perdition
In the pouring rain
You will search for me

Do not call me
Do not knock on my door
I will not be home

Find me in these words
In the middle of
Heaven and hell
Lost somewhere in between
The letters
Tortured somewhere in white space

I, too, will be looking for you and
This will be all that we have
I will search in silence
Mute or
Alive
With someone else or
Dead
Alone

I will be looking for
Your eyes
That passed by these words
Your eyes

That I used as a mirror
To see myself
I will look for you inside of this poem
That we created together

Maybe we will find each other
One more time
Just one more time
For the good times and
The tears

It will be hard

To catch fleas
Words
You must be dirty
You must be fast
You must jump and land and
Learn to suck blood,"

    I preached this, as Maricela guzzled her beer, leaving dark red lipstick marks on the Budweiser can. She smiled at my silliness. She lifted her fangs and laughed, "I'm Maricela, the vampiress!"

    "No," I countered, "Maricela, the flea."

    She dropped her head in defeat.

"This poem is not a curse
On the contrary
It is what you always wanted
What we always dreamed
But could not remember

We were always looking for each other
Will always look for each other
My love
Mari
We just did not know it
Until it was too late."

She lit a cigarette, pushed her brown hair out of her face, and smirked. She liked my stupidity, the truth of a lunatic.

When Maricela found out I died back in September of 91, she did not care. She took another hit off the yellow rock inside of the glass crack pipe and wandered off in the dark with some shadow. It took her some sobriety, some jail time, some loneliness, and the misfortune of routine to figure out she truly loved me. She had already been locked up a couple of weeks, when she found out she was pregnant. She did not realize it was mine until she started hearing the voices in her head.

"That fucking dog," she blasphemed inside of her cold jail cell and blamed me in her best gangster girl voice. It was too late for an abortion.

"That fucking dead dog

Your bark was loud
But you weren't vicious
You were actually pretty damn sweet
Misunderstood because of your muscles
Your lack of manners
I had to teach you

Without using a toilet
You shit on the streets
A dog you didn't even wipe your ass
I would scoop up your shit
With tender technique
Wrap it into a plastic bag
Throw it away
There wasn't no dignified way to do it

Therapy for dogs
Mindfulness for dogs
Miracles for dogs

None of it worked
You kept shitting on the streets
Bounced around smelling others' shit
Disgusting

Wrong
Happy

I talked to you
Sat you down
Looked into your eyes
Poured out the fire in my heart
The logic of a lady
You wagged your tail
Licked my face
Slobbered all over me
Loved me
Your master
Your mistress

Still
The next time I took you out
With full faith in your transformation
You still shit
I refused to pick it up
Finally exploded

'You fucking dog!'

You saw me
Finally saw me
Understood
But even with the understanding
You couldn't do nothin about it
And it broke your heart
Your ass was your ass
You had no hands
Only paws

We lived in
This imperfect relationship and
Yes
It was love.

Now you're dead, and all I got are our memories and this big belly. All I got are these voices that haunt me."

Mari knew no way out of the torture, and of course, I sympathized with her because I also heard these voices in my life. To deal with them, she tried to pray to me, but she did not understand that her prayers were my torture. She thought of me as El Santo, The Saint, but I am not a God. With all the power and hope I could muster in this strange ether, I lectured it to her, Maricela, who was so many eons away:

"Let's get this straight:

I never lied about
Forever
I may have been wrong
But I did not lie about it

In my being
Forever still lives
Even though
I do not

I am not a God
Was never
God

I was only ever a
Human
Thinking I was better and worse than
A God
But really just a human
Stubborn
Scared
Stupid
Sentient
Servant
Of existence
Trying to figure it out
Just like everyone else

Omnipotence is for
Control freaks
I know only what I know
And not even that

Still
I got shit done
Not like a God that
Waved his magic wand but
Like a man that
Stumbled and fell
Threw up in the gutter
Then
Kissed you deeply

It is not I who liked it
But you

You never wanted a God
Always sensed
I was imperfect
Someone who could be loved
Not worshiped

In your prayers
If I disappoint you
It is because of your
Lack of imagination
Not of Gods
But of monsters

Man being the most monstrous
Monstrosity of all."

I hoped she understood, yet she continued to pray, but only until the baby boy was born on Valentine's Day 1992. He was her new God. Chubby, chubby chubster, a totally natural baby boy born in lockup with his mother handcuffed to the bed to prevent her escape, to keep her enslaved to her place in the world. An ordeal of pleasure, pain, and fulfillment for Maricela, la mas *loca*. No drug could ever compare to the high of birth. She gave him my name, understood that there would be something special, something accursed about this Lil Santo. Perhaps she wanted to protect him with my spirit, as by that time the entire *varrio* had heard of my story of sacrifice that had catapulted me into street stardom.

But this stardom does nothing to help me in this other place. It is a phony sleep, where I remember myself sometimes and then travel to places, to ethers that are beyond anything I can explain in words, but this does not mean I keep nothing from Earth. I come back from a daze. I emerge from the abyss and sing to Maricela:

"I Forgot that I Forgot You

I am just now waking up
Rubbing the muck out of my eyes and
Remembering you
It has been a fogged up past
But I think
Once upon a time
You were too much for me

I used to call you *Mi Vida*
But lately I have not remembered even your name
Did it start with an "M"?
I forgot that I forgot you
What a sweet dream it was!
I forgot that I left you
I forgot that you are no longer here
My arms cannot reach out to grab your waist
I forgot that this other existence is bleeding
A hemorrhage of ripe red river
I forgot that I never found you hidden in the shadows
In the infinite galaxies

I hunted for days for years for eternity

43

And I still don't understand how I forgot you
Me
Who doesn't forget anything
Perhaps it was this
Death or
Dementia or
Cowardice or
A blessing
Oblivion
The answer to agony."

Hearing my song, Mari would wake up desiring me, but see only the baby in his crib. She would remember me when she would worship his fat face suckling on her nipple. I also sucked on those beautiful breasts, marked her all over her fierce red body, especially her neck and open chest, her navel and thighs. Making love to her, I would forget about myself and my misery. In the dark time before dawn, we still talk; the dead and the living communicate in that space between nothingness, when both sober and drunk people are sleeping.

"Maricela
I used to escape in you
Into you
Caught
Totally cornered and
At your whim

How could that have been,
Escaped and caught
At the same time?

I escaped in between your legs
Was caught
In your web."

The baby breathes, snuffles because he is congested. He is small Santo, Lil Santo. She is Mama Maricela, and she hears me.

"Santo," she whispers in response,
"I just played that
It was you who sucked my blood
I'm a Flea
Remember?

One time
I even told you
I wanted to chop my own head off
Instead of carrying around
The burden of your hickeys

But, yeah, it was me
Always me
Stealing your soul
Sucking *sangre*
Life blood
That's what fleas do."

Maricela giggles at the beautiful light brown baby boy, her true love. She does not suck his blood; instead she gifts him her milk. She is a cow. I am El Santo floating around nowhere.

I have learned
That nothing is what it is
Because she is no longer here
Gone
I do not know what to do
With myself

Yo sin su amor no soy nada

I am stuck. She, with all her aimless insanity and inconsistencies, is free. She sits in her cell, where little meek mice cuddle together in a corner. She rocks my son back and forth and gives him his life. She is a treasure. I do not blame her for fucking me over in life, for being a *Vida Loca Loca*, which was her duty from the start. I always knew what she needed to do.

45

"It was your destiny to leave me
First fall in love
Then get captured and
Finally escape

I am your prison
A cage
A stupid invention
To pretend
We can actually
Own or keep
Anything

We are nothing
All of us
Except you

You are a
Bird
That flies away
Leaving me again with
Nothing
But a
Song
And I sing and shout and cry it
And it keeps me from remembering
I am nothing

There is nothing I can do
You do what you want
That was always your
Destiny

Freedom

But only
Somewhat
More free

Because now
Unfortunately
You have a
Yearning for
Nothing
Because I was the best
Nothing
You have ever known

Even to the
Bird
That is
Anything
Sometimes
Nothing is
Beautiful

I am the
Cage
You chose."

"Fuck you, Santo," Maricela laughs and cries at the same time, her hair disheveled looking like a bird's nest. "You aint my cage. I am a woman," she says it with pride as the little boy sleeps so that one day he can become a man.

She is more than a woman, has more class than any of that. I sing for her suffering:

Sweet Fighting Lady

Brutal truth, soft truth
Fierce punches
Tender kisses
Never surrendering
Always *amor*
Forever fighting

Sweet Fighting Lady

She seeks justice
Without knowing or caring
It is impossible
A lie
She sticks to her
Truth
For better or worse
Stubborn
Stupid
Superwoman

A mother
A lover
Sexy body
Magic muscles
Not an intellectual but
A Witch
With her secret solutions
A woman who scares them all
Who they burned at the stake
Misunderstood
No
Not understood
Never understood

Sweet Fighting Lady

I love her exactly the way she is
I envy her
Her delusions
Her grand imagination
Her strong legs and
Action arms
Wonder Woman

She does not forget and
Because of that

She is forever fighting
Within herself
Knowing herself
Certainly
In torture
The test of a
Warrior Woman

Sweet Fighting Lady

****

That was yesterday.

Time melts, and I do not change. There, in that place, they change; they crumble and rise, the cycle of humanity. They stay worried about what that place means, worried about who they are. From outside, I would only whisper to my son Lil Santo, was afraid to corrupt him too much by speaking directly into him. I believe he listened. This was my duty as a father, to tell him just the way things are:

"Son
Anyone who tries to tell you the truth
Is a liar
Anyone who actually tells you the truth
Is a Saint
Anyone who lies to your face
Is a normal person
Who also lies to the reflection in the mirror

The world is full of these absolutes and inconsistencies
They are the same snakes
Everyone thinks they can solve the mystery but
There is no such thing as consistency
Things that are consistent are merely machines
That break like everyone else

Technology does not evolve us
Justice does not rescue us
Happiness does not fulfill us

Words damn you further
This is your curse
This is your blessing
These fucking words

Only you can ennoble
The stupidity of your suffering
And in the end
You will not even be here to laugh
At yourself

No stone will be left unturned."

Today, which is less than a wave crashing, in the year 2012, that wavy haired boy is a young man. Grown. Twenty years old. But he will always hold the title Lil Santo. He is almost older than me when I, at 21, vanished from that planet. No matter that he is rooted in *Vida Loca*, he does his own thing. Dark green tattoos, has em and inks em on others. Helps paint the murals on Balmy and on Clarion, all over *La Misión*. Smokes some weed. Wears baggy jeans drooping down, walks around with a backpack full of art and humility. He does not know me, yet I am there inside of him.

Yes, he hears the voices, as all of us hear the voices if we are being honest with ourselves. He, however, knows how to communicate with them, laugh with them, instead of letting them bully him around like I did in that place. It is strange how the son can become so different than the father. He is, in many ways, what I hoped I could have been.

Cool.

His first tattoo was the *Pachuco* cross on his own left hand. Indian ink against soft brown skin. Intimate art that he will never hide. Proof that he hears my whispers.

I do not worry about Lil Santo.

I also see that down there in June of 2012 there is the shadow of another boy, a foolish Cartoon, who has now grown into a full-fledged man. He is standing over me, my rotten bones, my tombstone, as he did twenty years earlier, and he still searches for something he does not know. I hear him.

"I've come all this way to see ya, Brother." The Cartoon fidgets in the beautiful blue day at La Raza Park Cemetery. "I can never forget you. I was there in 91, when Lobo came back with some sort of hit on you, but you were always El Santo, loved your Homeys even if they were there to murder you with a

Kill Kiss

All these years
I've learned
From you
Forgiveness
It aint no sin to be
Judas
Lobo
To be chosen
Since the
Beginning of time
For an important mission:

Betrayal

It's a horrible fate
To be chosen
To kiss and kill the
King of Kings

Judas
Lobo
I don't hold it against him
His terrible destiny
His bad luck
His brutal kiss
His imprisonment
If I got love
If El Santo meant anything
Then
Judas
Lobo
Too

Is my Brother."

Cartoon studies the tombstone, the language on the plaque. "Take Off." Cartoon is speaking out loud, "Lobo gave me the gat, and I didn't even know what the fuck I was supposed to do with it. You asked me to split with you, then we broke into the Ace Hardware Store on 29th Street. You started looking for saws, were playing with the Skilsaws, until you settled on a fat table saw that was in the back. I started searching for other shit to heist— toolsets, puzzles, spray paint, everything all around the store. Was having a good time. That's when I heard the noise.

I sprinted back top, right to the back of the store where all them table saws were, and I heard the machine going strong making the music of madness, the magnificent melody of machismo, the maestro orchestrating machine-guns trat trat trat trat. I stepped slow, maybe a little scared, unsure of what that noise meant.

I looked low.

You were in the corner of the room pushing something into the big saw. You were bent over reaching for something. Nah, you were leaning forward looking for something, and I crawled even slower cause I didn't want to shock you, didn't want to make you lose your place and lose sight of what you seemed to be lookin for.

I stepped small.

Looking down, I saw your feet planted solid. Your legs were locked up straight, the creases in your pants thick. Your chest was on top of the table. Your right hand was pushing the ON button. Your left hand was stuck in the ever-propelling saw, blood spurted out of it, and the *varrio*'s bloody fame was splattered all over the walls. Your chopped head was on the floor." Cartoon wipes water and salt off his face.

"You were the baddest *loco* I ever knew." He pauses in sincerity. "I got nothing except my low voice and these black roses to offer you." Cartoon places them on my tombstone. "I'm back here now in the hood, doin alright, but it still aint enough, these things I got now, this freedom I feel. It's just another word for nothin left to lose.

Yeah
There's purpose and pride
In me alone
But only for a moment

Laughing by myself too long
I lose my mind,"

Cartoon says it with a frown on his forehead.
He says it as if it is a serious thing! Cartoon continues,

"Independence is a great high and illusion
We chase after ourselves as if we could catch
The dust from stars

Independence ultimately equals selfishness
Boring unfulfilling stupidity

Unless we share
We can't have even proof
Of us
We never know ourselves

Community:
I need you in order for me to be me
You are my mirror
My liberation from myself
You save me from freedom."

My Cartoon looks down at my grave as if it can gift him anything.
He has been brainwashed beyond repair, yet I am proud of him. We are
all brainwashed in our own way, yet he chooses something more, part of
our tradition for others, *amor* in our special way, *amor* for his *varrio*, his
community.

I am his community. Spirit is his community. He knows it all, what
he needs to do, because simply by paying homage to the ancestors, for that
is what I am, he carries the fire. Matters of great concern should be treated
lightly. Matters of small concern should be treated seriously.

"Now I'm back to honor your memory. You already know that Lobo's
got Life in Q. He's been waiting for my return, probably read even more
books than I have, sure that he's thought more pensively than me. I'm gonna
see him, and we're gonna mastermind together, get us all ready to rumble. He
calls crazy shots, and that's what we need in the middle of this madness, of

us getting locked up, kicked out, killed. I just want to know, to ask you, what I need to do." Cartoon stops speaking.

What did he think I would tell him to do? To bust Lobo out? To initiate some new gang members? I have nothing to whisper to him, except to urge him to keep listening because in the silence there are secrets. In the Wolf's words there is wisdom.

It is a soft sunny day. The air is still. Not far off, you can hear children laughing and shouting in a school playground.

Cartoon will visit the lame, the sick, the imprisoned wise wolf, and then the good shit will start.

CHAPTER THREE — CARTOON

I blood-let, sacrifice my *sangre* through this ink.

My ancestors would cut their most intimate flesh and spread the pouring blood onto parchment paper, bark cloth that was then burned so that through the smoke that exuded from the flames, the spirits could snake out to reveal blessings—mysteries that drove a civilization to the stars and that were tattooed down in books, thousands of codices ultimately burned by the Spanish *Conquistadores'* holy men. Alone in this room, confined to myself, to my mind, to my pride and pain, I blood-let through writing so that I can communicate with spirits, so that I can share with you secrets burned away so many moons ago.

Para Purpose.

Nuestra purpose — because we are all in this thing together.

Unholy jungle of life
I know you
With your wicked webs and
Violent foliage
Mud deep
Hell heat

There is no escape

Therefore
I create my own existence
Independent of life's schemes for me

Imagining control
I stay ready
Listo
For life
Because it attacks with
A bang
A slash
A stab
A blessing

No matter your atrocities
Life
I love you still
I'm not ready for defeat
I stay ready for a kiss

But staying ready is hard. You gotta always be on point, but how can that happen when you don't have the most important tool they tell you that you need?

Education.

As a youngster, as the infamous Little Cartoon, my goal hadn't been to graduate from any school but to graduate to the pen. My purpose was the prison revolver. My older Brother was already inside, would later be killed in a prison riot. Young Homeys were also following the painful path. We were supposed to accept *la pinta* as our true education. In fact, inside the walls there were rules, codes, oaths, slick moves, and tough grading. A for assault, B for battery, C for chokeholds.

Mass incarceration in the age of colorblindness.

I was supposed to accept my death with a straight sober face, but how could I, when I'm a fucking Cartoon? Back then twenty years ago, I couldn't choose to not be a homeboy: that would've been blasphemy. But contrary to media bullshit, no one was forcing me to stay. There wouldn't have been reprisals if I decided to become a straight shooter. But I couldn't even fathom what the straight life meant. I was too obtuse to do anything in school. Even if I tried, I was so far behind educationally, academically, I would've quickly become disheartened. If I stayed in the hood, I would have chosen to be with my homeboys who were out there banging, selling drugs, getting locked up, and dying on the stinking streets.

It was Lobo who saved me, was Lobo who always had the insight to see into a future without an end. He realized we needed education.

He kicked me out back in 92, told all the Homeys not to fuck with me, not to give me any love. The restaurant owners wouldn't even sell me a *torta*! Fucking sly wise Wolf. So, without a *varrio*, I took off. Yeah, it was hard at first, but Lobo had given me some *feria*, so I didn't have to hustle too much except to get a job whenever I wanted a little more. I just traveled throughout these here United States, from one end of the big chicken to the other. I was like Toro, that tank, who had been in the Marines, adventuring to different shores, but instead of going overseas, I stuck to these here states, like Colorado, Kansas, Tennessee, Florida, *Nueva* York.

By 96 I was hustlin in the Big Apple, cause I had them big city itches in me, but I was reading, just picking up books and reading, taking some bullshit classes to get my GED, cause I had obeyed Lobo when he told me to, "Go get an education, young blood." My first critical text-based schooling had been Santo's tombstone (This is Take Off), and from there I just kept flying with the momentum of the wind. That's about the time I started writing, keeping a journal, but it was reading that first made me think I had any depth worthy to write about.

By reading I stole style. Reading, I've come to believe, is the key to consciousness.

When reading
You got to shut the fuck up and listen

What do you listen to?
Who do you listen to?

Not even you know
Cause that voice that enters into your brain is not your voice
You simulate a song of someone
You aint never met
You mimic an accent that slurs in your
Mute mind

You imagine somethin that cannot possibly be true
Yet you listen
And to do that you must be disciplined
Attentive and creative
Crazy
A Cartoon

To practice the skill of reading
You must be confident in your own

Nothingness

The denser the text

The more complicated and
Paradoxical the words,
The more you must question yourself and
Your own

Consciousness

It's a time of dangerous
Peace and safety
That forces you to construct your reality based on
Someone else inside of your
Mind

Will you be bullied?
Will you submit?
Will you find patience and humility to listen to someone besides yourself?
Are you exciting enough to entertain another brain inside of your brain?

A taboo point to proclaim:

Reading is the most magical message

The shit aint that hard once you put your heart into it. In the gritty
Bronx, where I rented a cheap closet, I started taking general education
classes. Without the community college system in place, I'd be caged
in prison or buried in a grave. On the streets I had learned to suffer and
to attack. Mixed with my stupidity, I was a lethal machine. I was bold,
yet extremely uncomfortable, awkward, and shy, unless you wanted to
spit vulgarity or deal with brute force. The frontline community college
system gives everyone, especially poor people, a thinking chance, one
that I desperately needed. My instructors loved me, saw something in me,
motivated me, especially the professors of color. They knew I was just like
the Homeys from the Bronx, but that I was different, too, that something
must have happened.

I started stealing ideas; that's the crux of a good education. I hogged the
same way James Baldwin hogged: "I will appropriate their white centuries,"
he declared in his celebrated short essay, "Autobiographical Notes." This
was also my solution every semester: "I'm gonna learn their ideas and add

my own sour twist to them, and maybe they'll realize brown represents more than just shit." My burning desire to learn fueled me to fashion someone beyond my jokes.

In spring of 98, I joined the speech team and debated at community colleges all over the boroughs and upstate New York.

"Once you refine your articulation and diction, you will be a very good speaker," one old lady white professor told me.

"Yes, Ma'am." I smiled and accepted her compliment but didn't accept her logic. She wanted me to talk like a white woman! By "refinement" she meant structured normalization, a system that would force me to smile superficially. I realized it had actually been good that I hadn't submitted to the school system in middle or high school cause then I would have been at best relegated to dullness; at worst, I would have learned to hate myself. Instead, because I made the stupid brilliant chance choice to feel this life, I got involved with lots of taboos—gangs, drugs, death, destruction, love, laughter, light—all of it without any school lens to analyze it. I felt it. I feel it. I felt the moment, the sublime and the suffering. I'm grateful that I refused the societal mass media mainstream brainwashing.

I also thanked Toro for giving me that bullheaded charge mentality. *Locura* was part of learning, too, and I loved my own street style. But, I gotta admit, the professors' praises for my critical thinking and speaking skills did give me confidence that I could achieve new ambitions. It felt good to think I could win a little bit. Writing out lists of life goals on pages of binder paper and pasting them to my bedside wall so I could wake up to them, I became a better thinker and planner.

Then I transferred to SUNY Buffalo, majored in political science, and graduated with a B.A. in 2001. Just as I had suspected, I got trained how to fucking smile and shake hands.

"Yes, sir, the pleasure is all mine."

In my mind and heart, though, I longed for the homeboy handshake.

I enjoy shaking dirty hands
Caressing the grime and calluses
That work hard for crumbs

Pure paws are healthy
Boring
Dangerous

Smooth skin sneaks stories
Of invisible dirt

What you don't know
Can hurt you
Clean happy hands tell lies

I knew that learning their lies was part of the game, and I wanted to know all their rotten apple corruption, inside and out, so I figured law was the route to power. I had to travel, though, cause that secret shit of law aint cheap. By 2002 I ended up in Arizona, the dry desert, hell heat, a place of traditional old school laidback *ese* style *cholos* y *cholas*. Was a good, reasonable price for a law school education, and I figured I'd be away from big city shit, so that I could focus on the manipulation of words.

In law school, in competition with mostly white people who were actually good ass thinkers, I felt the brash strategy of the streets wouldn't initially work, especially when I was so out of my league with the sly language and style of power. At Arizona State Law School, everyone was brilliant because they believed they were.

I didn't believe in the law, though. I didn't understand it nor care to understand it because I was so fucking mistrustful of it. In the law there were tricks purposely meant to confuse lower economic class people and keep them ignorant and, more insidiously, scared and hopeless. Simply to have a single legal form submitted to the court could cost you thousands of dollars in attorney fees. You weren't good, smart, or wealthy enough even to fill out the blank space designated for your own name, so you were supposed to hire a lawyer to do it! In fact filling out the welfare application form, something I had done for my moms since I was seven, was easier. We dealt with a welfare worker, who was kind of like us. To speak to a suspicious white wealthy lawyer or judge was to confess my utter stupidity and feel ashamed and angry. *Varrio gente* took that anger out not on the law, cause they knew how futile that fight was, but they took it out on themselves and other innocent destitute victims, until the *gente* were nothing but dry bones.

The law, you always knew, was an unrepentant killer.

Studying law, going beyond the rule of law, I started understanding that my tubby little illiterate mama was not really stupid. She used to holler *"No dejes que te laven el cerebro!"* Don't let them wash your brain! She was talking bout the streets, but it was also about so much more, the law, which is the power, the rhetoric, the media.

Learn your ABC of news
To surrender to what
Mickey Mouse wants
That rat owns
ABC

He's not playful
He is a vicious vermin
Who gnaws and scratches at your soul
That tastes better than cheese and is
Less sticky than peanut butter

You are the one trapped
In his reports about
Black people as savages
Brown people as stupid and
Snow White as beautiful truth

Silence is
BREAKING NEWS
Because it comes from within
From what is important
A discovery of depth
Without a voice

The only one
Brainwashing
You
Should be
You

That was my wisdom coming out of law school, three years of torture
and anxiety. I hated that shit, but am glad I went through it cause I had
to learn those things to be able to understand them better than the bosses
understand themselves, to be able to rebut them, but as far as any good is
concerned, I felt more fucked up than ever. I was smart but stupid as fuck if I

believed the law was truth. The entire formal educational institution tried to teach me writing is supposed to be all about references, precedent, citations, facts, and data. I finally figured out it's all bullshit.

One thing simply leads to another

Writing is the same way
One word to another word
A dog chasing its tail

There are no absolute definitions
One word forces you to another word
Scrambling for meaning
That is not there
Never was there
The dictionary
Created by a
Madman
Dr. William Chester Minor
Who sliced off his own
Dick!
As if to share that
Original
Action
Beyond the word
With the world

Stealing and sharing
That's the best we can do with our words

We're all plagiarists

Was I supposed to throw on a suit and oxfords now?
By 2007 I threw that justice *kaka* out the window for poetry, moved to mile high Denver, a tough town, and started going to underground cafes and just listening to and learning about *Neta*, pure unabashed truth. I couldn't abandon Lobo's command to go get an education, couldn't quit on him, so I went beyond law and formal education. Everywhere around me, they were

hunting to kill my spirit, calling me 'smart boy, good boy' which is worse than a Cartoon, and I almost submitted to their wishes when I had begun to think my shit didn't stink, that I was somehow better cause of degrees, pieces of paper that I can't even use to wipe my ass with. It was poetry that planted me back down to Earth.

It wasn't Shakespeare that got me into poetry, wasn't "to be or not to be." It was something more powerful, the reason for any poetry: Love.

I got disgusted with rhetoric, had built up an uneasy relationship with language, the politics of education and the infection of that disease's impact on the soul of writing. I thought education was supposed to give you power, but it was just an institution, economic and political power simply for power's sake, a puppeteer power's sake because it wasn't even real for the masses. In school I learned their structures of writing, but I didn't know how to really write or read. It took love for me to learn how to write and read. I'd been searching for *Neta* without realizing it can only be found in Love. On napkins I would reflect and write down in the most beautiful calligraphy *cholo* style writing "I Love You. *Por Vida*" and I'd mean it, always meant it, gifted that poem away with all my heart to the women I love. Little love napkins. I treasured those napkins, but in order to truly treasure poetry you gotta be willing to give it away, the entire napkin: all of your heart, all of your soul. I love, I loved, but also never allowed myself to love—because I had a duty to my brothers, that duty I accepted when Lobo told me to "get an education, young blood," duty to Santo's spirit and to the pledge I made for our people. I knew one day I would have to go back to *La Misión*, so I could never let myself settle down.

My mission, my blessing, was to find something and sacrifice myself totally in the process of poetry. Sparse words. I grew from those words, realizing it was the simple words that held the highest meaning, and there is really only one word in everything important I read, in everything substantive I write: *Amor*.

Amor is the beginning of poetry. It gave me courage and insight that then showed me the outside. It was poetry that showed me our culture can't be killed.

Patronize me
Bully me
Oppress me
Mock me

Murder me
Tell me I'm all fucked up
I need that from you
Your manners and etiquette
Your command:

"Be A Good Person"

I better be a
Good boy
And break down each
Word
So I can understand your
Genius

Is this what you mean?

Be:

Not my existence but
Your existence
Your air
Your being is what it means
"To be"—
Hamlet lied—
There is no
"Not to be"
All being is you
What you say it is
Trademarked by your
Flag of force
No other reason to live except for your
Disneyland dreams and
McDonald's mansions
Those golden arches
Guiding me to
The entrance of pearly gates
Glittering estates

Full of flowers and
Green grass
Green dollars
Fluorescent green glowing from
Nuclear blasts
Lay on the sweet bed of being
Don't worry
You will not melt

A:

Like the Fonz
"Ayy"
Thumbs up leather jacket milk smile
A
Happy Day
Which is
Singular
No plural community
Only one
Alone
Independence in the manner of
Good old fashioned American independence
Selfishness sickness
You can do it without others
This place is yours for the taking
Manifest Destiny, Homes!
A
A
A
A luxurious lie
A horrible hoodwink
A deception to make you believe that simply
Pulling yourself up by your
Bootstraps
Is possible for the majority of you all
When the majority of you all got
Giant red

Bullseye targets
Tattooed on your backs
The day you were born

Good:

Now we get to the
Good
Stuff
Morality ethics principles scruples decency
Purity
Clean
WHITE
Look it up in the dictionary cause it's right there for all to read:
Of the color of pure
Snow
The opposite of Black
(Brown, of course, is shit)
Innocent
Without evil intent
Honest
Honest
God is White
Blonde hair blue eyes
Be good
Like God
Who makes the laws and
Breaks the laws yet
Expects you to abide by them nonetheless
Be part of this paradox
Good good good boy
Pat you on the head like a dog or
Massacre you on the street like a bad

Person:

Homo Sapien
Latin for "wise man"

(No stupid shits allowed)
Human being
A worthy vessel of existence
Not some fucking
Hunched over monkey savage animal
Indio
But a real live erect walker
Straight like a hard dick
Sometimes he even holds that name
Like Dick Nixon
AKA
Tricky Dick
AKA
President Richie Nixon
A person like that
Nice and normal
Upright
Walking and talking that game
Commanding you
"Be A Good Person"
And you gotta salute and respond
"Aye, Aye, Sir"
Cause that's the fucking commander in chief
A good person

Our Culture Cannot Be Killed

Skulls and *cholos*
Aint got no good people
We got the dregs from the gutter
The mamas from the fields
The papas from the prisons
The kids from the streets
We got color but it aint bright
It's dark
Gruesome green
Battered blue
Beat down brown

Righteous red
A rainbow of reality aint no good but it's better
Than a command to what I know is
Worse
Gentrification of the mind
Assault on authentic ideas
An unloving of
Myself
Of my
People

You be a good person
I love my *gente* too much to betray them
Together in hell is better than your heaven

These revelations from poetry were authentic education that nobody had to pay for and also that nobody paid you for! That's what they trick our youngsters to believe about education: it aint worth nothing unless you make money off of it. That was the same message the techies were bringing to the hoods, too. Shit, I'd rather be hungry and conscious than fat and happy.

But the blessings of consciousness aren't easy. You get into a funk and see things for what they are. You look back at the pages you've produced. You understand it's the wretchedness of who you are.

The page is swarming with insects
Fleas and cockroaches
Spider symbols

In the trash
There are dead ideas and poems
The songs of dead friends I no longer have

Now the night of Tequila is all that remains
The night that knows nothing else but to howl
And I will puke up my soul in the morning
As if it were a magic trick
As if it were a blessing

But we all know we make too much of ourselves
The soul stinks
Not like a flower
But like the vomit that it is
Corrupted
Killer
Premeditated
First degree murderer that deserves
Eternal damnation

One day the night will never end
You will become numb even to your own pain

Sometimes even the devil weeps

In 2009 I scattered through Texas and started washing dishes to keep
my mind right, to learn and feel truth. I needed something beyond mind,
so I learned to feel the water on my hands. I saw and felt the smiles on the
Homeys' faces coming to work, how they would share their crystal meth with
each other, to keep each other going, these functional crystal *paisa* border
brothers, who had to work two jobs, sixteen hours straight to feed their
families back in El Salvador, Honduras, Mexico. Learned so much from their
love, like how we'd abandon the kitchen for a few hours to rest, come back,
and the pots and pans would be greeting us touching the ceiling! But it never
fazed us, cause we'd grab the hoses and have a big ass water fight, soaking
each other and getting shit done. For me this was more enlightening than
even law. I admired their real hard work and genius, the guts to have dignity
outside of the system's brand of intelligence.

Don't trust wicked words or
Twisted eyes
Foolishly
They try to make sense of illusions

The only thing that matters is
Feeling
Gut loves salt and sugar and
All that is bad

Spirit loves ghosts
That never show their faces

How can it be that the sweetest lie is
The most bitter truth?
And that we should love it nevertheless!

Truth?

What is that except what I feel and
If my feeling is false then
There is no doubt
That everything else is
Less than truth

Only love knows no limits
Not even truth
Not good or
Evil
Or what I thought I knew about
Myself

Love beyond logic:
Better to enter
Paradise
Without eyes
Than to be damned to
Hell fire
With
Twenty
Twenty
Vision

    Maybe I was repeating the same themes; that's what happens locked
up in a hole. Everything turns to a blur. I dedicated myself to writing, like a
monk pledged to prayer. I felt El Santo, the spirit, actually felt his complex
spirit, guiding me to these unseen truths. By 2010 I wrote *Barrio Bushido*,
the story of us, for no one except myself. Years passed, ten, more than fifteen.

At that point I moved back to a big city cause I just couldn't shake them roots, so ended up freezing in Chi-town, sitting in the notorious Southside smoking hand-rolled cigarettes and staying out late, *solo cholo* for the most part, and I could see myself from somewhere else, like a third person experience. I was just a man, a homeboy who wrote nothing but poetry.

Couldn't tie my shoes
Nor take apart an engine
I understood the abyss
Believing it was separate from my own
Destruction
Trusting I could outwit the omnipotent
With the power of word

Me but not me

The Homey who wrote nothing but poetry
Sacrificed pussy and petty pleasure
Abandoned his own potential
For days and weeks he would not speak
Refusing conversation and chit-chat
Repudiating whispers so
He could save up might
For the magic of
Just
One
Word

A whirlwind
A damnation
A heaven
Then the *vato* who wrote nothing but poetry
Would dance in the dead-end alleys
On the rooftops
Alone he would bop
Strangers would think he was shadowboxing
But he was actually in bliss
The sublime

The goal that cannot be got

The man who wrote nothing but poetry
Did lots of drugs
Was dangerous
He wanted his life to be just like a poem
With fire and stone
Water and wood
Diamonds and uranium
A fake forever

He would wake and write
Hunched in his hole hammering away
His neighbors thought he was a fool
For relying on rhymes that writhe
Images that fade
Metaphors that make no sense
That no one would even read
Worthless words
Lost life

The man who wrote nothing but poetry
Wandered the streets mumbling
Sometimes screaming
He refused to squander his precious words
On those who could not understand
Would never understand
He felt poems were friends
That would never betray
But the man who wrote nothing but poetry
Deluded himself

The words cried
The words lied
The words died

Sometimes the man who wrote nothing but poetry
Could not write a line

It crushed him
Eventually he gave up
Love and people and pets and style

The homeboy who wrote nothing but poetry
Ate only poultry
Wore nothing but rags
Would walk around barefoot on crushed glass
His teeth fell out of his face and
He would venture out only at midnight
Which is the witching hour
The hour of poetry
Then he would pray his poems
Sweating blood
Enchanting spirits

And that was enough
To be his own God

The Cartoon who wrote nothing but poetry

And this spirit through writing poetry gave me strength, courage, an understanding more than any degree I had ever earned, but I knew something was missing. I knew "I," but what the good fuck is I without a you: community?

It's easy to be a monk on top of a lonely *loma*. I had paid my debt to Lobo. I had obeyed his instructions and gotten my education, but it wasn't no bachelor's degree or juris doctor that was the real knowledge; it was life itself, the school of hard knocks and washing dishes, working construction, roofing, shoveling snow, and being with a woman one night and loving her, even wanting a family, but never letting myself stay stuck, postponing even *amor* for what I knew needed one day to get done. Staying hungry, lean, running early mornings. I needed not education, but hunger to learn.

Soledad

Living with your hunger
Is the same as

Living with your suffering
It is the balance and
The price of
Power

When someone has learned
How to be alone with his suffering
How to kill his desire to escape
All the illusions others share
Then he has reached another level

I will
Live and die
As a
Vida Loca
Loco

For what does it mean to be a writer if you do not write what you live
and live what you write?

Twenty years passed too quickly. Earlier this year in 2012, I didn't even
know how to go back, didn't really even want to go back. Go back for what?
All the *varrio*s were the same, New Mexico, New Orleans, East L.A. There
is no way back, is there? I felt stupid, useless. And in anger and frustration, I
kept saying fuck this, fuck that, fuck all this shit during these hard times, and
that is exactly what turned out to be the answer, my personal epiphany.

Maybe there was a way to go back, a time machine that could rewind us
to something else.

Yes.

Fuck You Is a Time Machine

When you say it
Sincerely
When you maddog them in
Their eyes
Burn it into their flesh
When you declare it with
Conviction and faith

Fuck You is a time machine

Overall
Things have not gotten better
They are worse
Technology has not solved our problems
We are more
Anxious
Distracted
Brainwashed
Butchered

With Fuck You
The future can be different
It does not improve with
Etiquette or
Education or
Civilization
The best solution is a
Time machine
That we all hold to say
Fuck You
To refuse
Their lies
Their hoodwinks
Their hypocrisy

Handshakes or
Handjobs
Do not do the job
A time machine
Rewinds us
Puts us there
At that exact moment
When Cortez or
The Pilgrims or
The politicians landed

Fuck You

Establishes respect
Gets us ready for revolution

Sometimes you don't even
Have to say it
Just know it

Fuck You

And you will be in your
Dream
Then
A change is gonna come

I saw gentrification happening in hoods all over, Nueva York, Seattle, Albuquerque, but most importantly, I heard and read about it happening in my own hood, SFM, *San Fran* Mishon, literally the most expensive corrupted *varrio* on planet earth. Everywhere I went that was being gentrified, the poor people, my compatriots, my brothers and sisters, told the same story. The techies knew better what to do with the *gente* than the *gente* knew what to do for themselves. The techies sang the opera of technology, justified their greed and inhumanity by singing the garbage of evolution, that it was for the Natives own good, eventually, that they submit to the power of technology because it was so perfect and beautiful.

Don't be stupid, accept your doom with a happy face :)

I learned to listen to the wind and love my people, no matter where I was in America. That *amor* had been the goal of my education, an education that is everywhere at all times, and that's when I knew it was time for me to go back, face Lobo, and force a change, to that summer of love city, where they used to sing about wearing a flower in your hair.

San Francisco
San Fran
Frisco
The Sco

Saint Francis
The man of love and suffering
The stigmata *sangre*
Convinced the wolf not to eat the people
A hero
A myth
A traitor to treasure
He worshipped poverty
Called birds and beasts
Brothers and sisters

1967:

The Summer of Love
Golden haired hippies in
Golden Gate Park
Flower power
Free love
Free weed and acid
Naked bodies dancing
Tye dye peace symbols spinning
Ultimate utopia

At the same time
In the same place

Highrise projects
Army Street
Armed robberies
Assaults
Abandoned Black and Brown people
Desperate flowers suffocating out of cracked concrete
My father and mother making a family
My oldest Brother
Amor in a little room
Because outside there aint love
You are not a hippy

2012:

45 years later
The Summer of Hate
Gold and greed
Property an evil imagination
Gentrification
Techie hipster cafes and
Cheese schools
Educate the new gel-bearded breed
Line the streets where not even hippies are allowed anymore

Now

They celebrate the nostalgia of being
The most liberal place on planet earth yet they
Harass the homeless
Kill the poor
Eat the babies
Salute the Nazis
Most of the *gente* from 67
Kicked out
Maligned
Exterminated

The Summer of Love
Turned to Fall
Ended in the dead of winter

Saint Francis
Where are you
In your own city?

Saint Francis
Where are you
To talk with the beasts?

Saint Francis

Do you bleed
Inside of your palms
In the middle of your feet?

Saint Francis
Will you save us
This time?

Or is it up to us
The outcasts
To come back and make
San Fran
Frisco
The Sco
What it was always meant to be?

The Wild West

CHAPTER FOUR — MAMA MARICELA

Even though Santo used to call me Mari, don't mistake me for Maria, a virgin Mary, cause I aint never been her. I was fucked the first time I ever took a breath. Here aint no sad innocent story.

Maricela means I'm from Mars, the God of War, bitch! The Tsunami hits and splashes me to wherever it wants, but I swim like a shark, jumping out of the waves, singing a song at the beginning of each war, each day, to the morning shower

Fuck a bath
I refuse to lay down and die
A warrior woman
I stand
A drunk
I push the wall
A cold waterfall helps
Cure the worst hangover

The shower solves
My dirt
Nastiness
Inadequacies and
Despair

A luxury
A necessity
A healing
A stall
For thinking
For crying
For singing
For sanity

A place of freedom
Where we're unashamed of our
Nakedness
The water hits us and

We're happy

The pitter patter of rain is
Morning hope
Soap is medicine
Shampoo is wisdom
Steam is serenity

It is a new day

     After drying myself off, I plop down in my little yellow kitchen and cook my breakfast like a nice lil old lady of 44. Lil Santo is grown, 20 years old. He can cook his own damn eggs.

Beautiful breakfast
You inspire me
With your two eggs and *tortillas*

But it's my duty to eat you

So I'll chew slowly
Respectfully
I won't swallow you whole
My fat mouth overstuffed with
Onions tomatoes and worries

The sun shines morning
A time for possibilities
Last night was darkness and torture
Today the coffee is hot
The children skip to school

There is a future
In a bowl of oatmeal

     Mornings like this I remember myself, a time before I was such a bitch.
     Folsom Park on 21st Street, a cold autumn Sunday morning in 1975, we wore light sweaters. In the desolate schoolyard, the steel wheels whirring, the

cold didn't matter. My daddy had fired me off, and now the bike and me were one hot bullet. Both me and pops thought that if I could control the chaos of the two wheels, I could control the world. But my dad hadn't really believed, but now here was undeniable proof that his little seven year old girl was ready for total truth. He watched me smiling and riding, the wind striking my face and hair, and I was fearless, using my own propelling momentum to battle the power of the universe. Everything was new and open and free. Pops pulled out a crumpled damp cigarette from his sweater's hip pocket. Although the wind didn't want to let him, he lit it, slick style nonetheless. My father must have felt a mixture of happiness and sadness for what he knew he needed to do.

"Mari, *mi* Maricela!" He praised me. Looking up to heaven, he exalted me. He shouted as I escaped him, as he prayed I could forever remain his little girl. As if I could read his mind, I turned the bike around because I would never have left my papa. I raced back towards him, a woman. He bowed his head to me, squatted on his knees, and welcomed back his little queen.

"Papa, Papa! I did it, Papa! I did it all by myself!" My candied brown teeth were sweeter than the cheap candy I many times ate as my lunch. As I dismounted the bike, my father embraced me and kissed my open mouth. Together, we hugged in the middle of the lonely gigantic playground of the cosmos.

"I am proud of you Maricela," he said it with a bitter smile. "You have now done what for the longest time was impossible; with only your independence, you have sped faster than men sped for thousands of years." I looked at him strangely because I didn't completely understand the meaning or intent of his words.

"Yeah, Papa, I did good!" To control the cold, I stuffed my hands into my pants pockets.

"Yes, *mija*," my father grabbed both of my small shoulders, "and now you have the power to do even better."

"What can I do now, Papa? Papa, I have done it all!" I gyrated my body to let loose of his grip.

"Maricela, now you can do more than *todo*!" My father let me go, maybe so I could freely accept his advice of my own convictions. He stood up to look down at me. "We are *Indios*. This is the first and last time you'll ever hear those words from my mouth. I am an *Indio*, even though they tell me I am American. Your mother is gorgeous, but she aint like me. With her blue eyes, she comes from a family that believes in the purity of snow. When I met and won her, because that was my desire, the snowflakes all abandoned her. That is why our family is so alone living in the Mission."

I strained my neck up to look into my father's eyes.

"No matter what ever happens, now you know, and you must know. It's my duty to tell you." My father could not help but stutter before the truth. "Maricela, in this world, we have but one thing that is important: our spirit. With *espíritu* anything is possible. You have not heard me ever speak in this way to you before, but you have heard my spirit through the actions I have led. You know of *Indios* through my dancing and my winking and my way with words." I nodded my head, took my hands out of my pockets, and rubbed my cold ears with my warm palms. My dad took my left hand and began walking with me around the playground, leaving the bicycle in the middle of it all.

"My words have sounded like others' words because I've wanted them to sound like others' words. Because that is the way of those in this place. Like your mother. They believe in the words of America and the words of the teachers and the words of the politicians. With those words, they deceive themselves without even knowing they are deceived. But in you, I see the spirit of truth." He stopped and stooped down to me, so that he could measure my eyes.

"Yes, daddy, I understand that the spirit is most important." I shocked him with my genius.

"Then you understand that the words don't matter. That it is you who matters in this place. But since the others hear only words, you can't expect to teach them or help them or love them through words. Your spirit must show you and them the way."

"But, daddy, if they hear only words, what good are words? Why do we talk, Papa?"

"Only a star could think of such questions." He pet my soft, tangled brown hair and gazed into my sea green eyes. "We talk in order to deceive; that is the purpose of words. This is the most important lesson I can teach you about words: Words are lies, *mentiras*. Know this, accept this, and you can have anything in this world that you want. Words are lies."

"Papa, I don't understand. You are scaring and confusing me." My eyes welled with salty water.

"No, Mari, you cannot allow even my words to hurt you. You must believe in my spirit. What does my spirit tell you? What does your spirit tell you?" I closed my eyes to hear the silence of his spirit. I squeezed my eyes even tighter to listen to my own hushed whispers. I listened to voices that were mine yet not mine, voices that existed in the ether. I didn't know how much time had passed because time did not exist nor matter. Finally, when I opened my eyes, I breathed in a powerful deep breath. I looked at my father who was waiting on bent knees, fixed on my eyes.

"You love me, Papa. I love you, Papa," I said it with certainty and pride and a spirit of one and all.

Totally amazed, physically dizzy, my father sat down on the cold concrete so that he could keep himself from falling. Now I was looking down at him.

"*Mi* Maricela, you have heard and spoken the spirit, the true spirit, so the words do not matter. In fact, the words mean nothing compared to what is in your heart. This is the most beautiful gift I can give you: As long as you know and believe in the spirit, the words can be lies. Do you understand?"

I looked down at my poor Papa, and for the first time noticed his graying hair, cared that his front teeth were missing, judged that his nose was too fat and his black eyes too shifty for love.

"Yes, I think I understand."

"Mari, you must understand." He didn't want to give me any further hints. Either I would know it now or be forever confused, just as America, just as San Francisco itself was confused and lost. "Maricela, with words, with the words coming from your mouth, tell me the truth." It was his eyes that now welled with water, and I pitied him. I studied the dirt in the middle of the cracks in his face, the blemishes left by years of greasy eating, drinking, and smoking. His clothes were tattered, holes peppered his gray cardigan sweater, and dirt infected his fingernails that were too long.

I calmly closed my eyes. In the darkness, I felt his chapped lips kiss me goodnight. I saw his droopy yellow eyeballs greet me with pancakes in the morning. I heard his growling and gnashing of teeth that was supposed to be singing. I remembered how people looked away at his teeth, the holes in his mouth, when he smiled confidently. I remembered that even with his shirt off he had only bones to display. I thought about why some children refused to play with me.

"I hate you. Father, I hate you," I commanded it with a calm composure. We locked onto each other's spirit. I didn't look away. There were no tears, no remorse. I stood straight with my arms dangling at my side.

He believed me so much that it broke his heart. When he rose from his knees, I didn't look up. He picked me up off the ground and raised me up above him, spinning me around in circles. I smiled the biggest Maricela smile.

"I love you, Mari. *Te amo*, my little *India*." It was he who cried as I embraced the heavens that awaited me, while his tears fell to the simple Earth. When he let me down, I dashed to retrieve my bike.

The next day he took off forever. A couple of years after that my heroin addicted mama OD'd, and I was left to the streets of *La Misión*.

The years and tears passed.

Mornings like this, sipping on my second cup of black coffee, I remember that fuckin nut, *El Santo*, my savior. It was 1990 when we first met at about ten or eleven in the morning at the Salvation Army on Valencia and 26th Street. I was hunting for ho clothes, cheap stuff. He was looking for more. He stood straight, saw me in my pink mini wrapped around my tight ass, and just walked up to me, not like a john or a pimp, but like a man, all fucked up and honest.

"I shop for love at *La Segunda*," he said it, and I blushed and thought to myself *What a pickup line*! Yeah, I liked him. And he kept goin like if he wasn't even talkin to me.

"The Salvation Army
The thrift stores
The dumps

Here
There is no need to wish for a sale because
Every day you are guaranteed
A cheap second-hand happiness."

Santo studied and caressed a moth-eaten checkered red Pendleton board shirt.

I had nothin better to do, thought he might at least have a good time. I agreed with him.

"These are the clothes
The rags
The love of
The departed

85

The foreclosed on
The abandoned
The hand-me-downs that
Can't be handed down anymore.

It's a good deal for us, *loca*s and *locos*." I smiled at him cause he may
have been weird, but he was fit and hard, a stylish *cholo* with wavy dark
brown hair, a handsome young man before that evil bitch Time would have
eventually got him. How's that saying go? Live fast, die young, look good in
your casket. Yeah, that was Santo.

"We are special strangers." He stopped being somewhere else, talking to
someone else, and looked at me, into me; he had that talent. "We will never
hope for the fairytale," Santo said it with pride.

"We wish for
Utility
A cold kiss
Not perfection but
Satisfaction
Enough."

It was a good point, but it wasn't everything. Maybe I should have just
cared about pulling some cash out of him, but how the fuck stupid would
I have been to pretend myself Pretty Woman lookin for Prince Charmin at
The Salvation Army? Nah, was better that I slapped this homeboy with some
truth.

"I settle for leftovers cause," I swallowed my breath, paused, then let it go,
"because
I'm a sinner
Brown
Guilty
From the gutter

No matter how much
Wealth
Wisdom or
Will

86

I own
I aint nothing but
The worst,
A woman."

Yeah, I said it instead of pretendin some ho-stroll fronting.

Santo nodded, gave me mutual respect. Motherfucker was a feminist without even knowin what that word meant! He was quiet for a few seconds, too long, when I should have just walked the fuck away from this *loco cholo*.

"The stale cigar smoke
Permanently reeks on
This dead man's
Classic plaid Pendleton
Now it is mine."

Santo hugged the shirt he had been holdin, and I thought of myself in his hard arms.

"I like that smell," I told him.

"The smell of the streets
Keeps me honest."

He smiled with his eyes, and that was it, I guess our first date, and yeah, it was love at first sight, that fuckin plague that can't keep anyone honest.

The beauty of cowardice
Can only be appreciated by liars

They understand what it is to sin and sin
To sin without mercy or expectation of miracles
To appreciate betrayal is to appreciate
Art in its finest form

For this there's only one compensation
The one we all seek and serve:

Death

No more, no less

To love without limits is
The talent of a traitor

You must surrender this life

By surrendering
You find it
There
In the middle of madness
There
In the open sewer
There
In your bed
Tousled in between the sheets
You find it
Such betrayal
Such beauty
Long hair
Soft skin
Closed eyes

Imagination
The taboo
Lies
What we all pray for

Whoever is honest
Can never love
The beyond

Whoever lies
Goes straight to hell

It was one hell of a ride being in love with a Saint, not the saint of
Christianity, but the saint of the *cholos*. He was your fuckin man. I saw how

they all worshipped him—Lobo, Toro, and that runt Lil Cartoon. Santo made everyone sick with it. He made me sick, too, but instead of me worshipping him, the great good lookin Santo worshipped me, a dime a dozen bitch.

What a crazy world?

I was sexy, slutty, real juicy, curvy ass and all. Loved showing off my painted ladies toes in sandals. Sick with it in a way that was outside his understanding.

The *locura* of a lady.

We partied a lot together, everywhere, Carlos' Bar, Garfield Park, Mission Dolores, Bernal Heights, sometimes with the other Homeys: Lobo, Toro, and Lil Cartoon would always be hanging around. On many a night, I witnessed Santo's spiritual transformation—from somewhere way back that we just didn't know or understand anymore. He was like my dad, but he had never even known his own dad, some Irish fool—Santo didn't even know for sure. But his mama had been a *Mexica India* from Zacatecas. I knew something was wrong with him. Something had happened a long time ago. He would drink so he could cry.

Firewater
From hell
Helps to bring out
All those good
Evil spirits that need
Exorcism

There are too many
Fake horror stories
On TV
In theaters
Amongst the dead

Real horror is alive
Watch a drunk *Indio*
And you will
Shake in your boots
Shit in your pants
You'll know something
Horrible is happening

Something horrible happened
Inside of the *Indio*'s spirit

Talk to a drunk *Indio* and
You will never be the same
Make love to a drunk *Indio* and
You will be impregnated with
Firewater sperm

He will be born
You will baby him
Help him and he will
Throw it all away
Because he is history
Firewater horror history

Tecun Uman
Running Bull
Crazy Horse
Tupac Inca Yupanqui

The *Indio* is born again
In firewater
And that is why
Never
Under any circumstances
Should you give liquor or
Love
To an *Indio*

    Even with Santo's green eyes, just like mine, you could tell by his tawny brown skin that he was a fuckin *Indio*, an insult to the core. Like me, he was half European mutt and half *Indio*, which is 100 percent all fucked up. Santo fell in love with me even though he knew what the price would be. Gangster girl. Better than anyone else's bullshit. And I remember the last time we saw each other, before he fucking chopped off his own head. I knew who he was. I knew who I was. I was hittin the pipe. It was a spooky night.

The night of the living dead
The night of *La Pura Neta*
It's a night of the beyond
Not sublime and not hell
The essence of existence
Truth
Which is horror and love
At the same time

In between the shadows
It is there
He is there
Posted
Standing solid
A *Vida Loca*
Loco
El Santo

I will never again witness
Someone in such stupid agony and
Clear confession
Who
With sweet sincerity
Looking into my eyes
Declares to me
That he is a
Piece of shit

I don't understand what I see
Am mute to his misery
Because it's not my dream
But the opposite of it

His song is for ears that never wanted to hear:

"Sometimes in the middle of the
Nothing
You get the urge

To destroy something beautiful
I think you were always destined for me
The worst thing that ever happened to you"

With this
I know my power
I can help him or
Run away
The truth has always been mine

I found out I was pregnant while I was locked up. Had the baby while I was handcuffed to the hospital bed. No drugs, all natural. Maybe it was fucked up, but I told you, I aint Mary in a stable surrounded by shepherds; I'm Maricela from Mars, the God of War, El Santo, and he would never have loved me any other way. Shit, my shepherds were the guards that I hustled throughout my pregnancy.

But I kept faith in something, I don't know what, thinking of Santo, hearing his voice whisper in the wind on the prison yard, and even though he was dead, I knew he was with me, and no doubt that motherfucker didn't give a fuck and neither would I. No matter how fucked up we were, we had love, just like my idol, Frida Kahlo, whose image is hit up all over these Mission walls. Yeah, I guess she helped me, too, with her life and art, through those years locked up, down and out—me imagining Santo like Diego and me like Frida.

Original

Always outrageous
Unaccepting
Authority

Mujer
Warrior Woman
Wearing *Huipil*
Flower headdress
Coral and jade necklaces
Guatemalan sashes
Matriarchal regality

Pain
Dolores
The root:
Polio and an awful accident
Crippled her but it was
Consciousness
Too
Cause without that agony
She could see only
In front of her

Miscarriages
Heartbreak
Sickness
The amputation of a leg
Forced her to find other ways
To move
To fly

Art
Painting
Suffering
Loving
Amor
All of it twisted into
Colors and creativity
Absurdity

Frida and Diego were
Disloyal and divorced
But they never betrayed
Each other's essence
Got hitched again
In San Francisco and
Stayed faithful to their
Shared *locura*
They were artists

Eccentric
Impossible

She stayed through his affairs
Even when he loved Frida's own
Sister
Diego stayed through her sickness
Held her hand
As she died
As she won

In the end
Frida
Proved
Nothing is taboo

    Santo won this one, my main man, my only Saint. And unlike Frida and
Diego, we had a baby together, and even War, *La Loca* Maricela, loves her
own child. Me and Santo, my very own Diego Rivera, made magic, love.
Like an artist I created something that only I could do, and I knew it was
God, a Lil Santo light skinned *Indio*, a little miracle that taught me some
tenderness.

I'd rather create than destroy
Creation liberates
Destruction confines

I'd rather sing than curse
Songs cure
Curses cripple

I'd rather dance than sit
Dancing dares
Sitting sucks

I'd rather love than hate
Love laughs
Hate cries

I know
I know
How stupid I am
For wishing
For ignoring the torture
All around us

But I'd rather be an idiot with life
Than a smart ass with death

Sometimes we need
Lil miracles
Of our own action
Sometimes these are more than enough
For another day
Another night

The sun shines at six o'clock
Every morning

I would see the light. Five years in the can, get up at six in the morning, get ready for chow, out the cell, eat some grub, back in the cell. Lil Santo, my miracle child, stayed with me for a few months, then had to go to a foster home, but I didn't forget him. In 1997 I got out, moved to a spot on Shotwell Street, and got my baby back. He grew into a good young man.

One afternoon back in 2006, in his sophomore year in high school, he started whisperin to me words like his father, talkin bout love and *amor*, tryin to find his way in the world. Goin through puppy love and lots more, killings on the streets, fake schooling, new white people moving in and lookin at him like he's the crazy one.

"Mama," he looked like a damn yellow-brown puppy, "What does a man do with all the love he has in his heart?" He got green eyes just like his papa, just like me, green grenades, and though he doesn't gangbang, he got this holiness about him.

I smiled, but also wanted to slap him upside his head. This is what I taught my son:

"Do You Know How Men Should Love?

Soft and smooth
Not rough like a pit bull
But serene and sound
Full of nobility and magic
Honor
Opened doors
Bowed heads
Gentle kisses on gloved hands

Romance

However,

Men are stupid
And what should be
Is different
Than what is
Reality

Men make everything
Ugly and bloody
Big muscles
Scruffy stubble
Loud farts and
Alcohol arguments

Do you know how men should love?

They should abandon it all
Even the title of
Man
Give it all away
Especially love
To everyone
Everything
In every way

Not special
Not macho
Just gift it the way it is
The way you found it
Tasted it
Natural
Sometimes
Sweet
Sometimes
Sour
Inside of every apple
There is a secret destiny

A rock
A tree
A cloud

These are things a man
Should know how to love
In order to love."

    Lil Santo liked that, I could tell by the way his jaw dropped. He didn't
know his mama had game like that, but he then made the mistake of thinkin I
was some sort of philosopher like his papa, cause he kept questioning me.
    "But why does it have to be so hard: love?" Lil Santo must have been
going through it. He was almost shivering as he asked it.
    "Sometimes it just be's that way, honey. Love aint got no grudge against
you. It just is what it is." I stroked his wavy brown hair, tried to be tender
mama.
    "It's unfair," he pouted. "I know I give so much love to others, feel
my pops in everything I do, but they don't love you back in the same way,
mama! Love is supposed to be only beautiful." Santito stomped his foot on
the kitchen floor. I lost my patience, had to be a homegirl.
    "Whoever said shit was supposed to be fair?" I was irritated cause I
knew both me and his papa Santo had already figured out the racket by his
age. That's why I make him cook his own damn eggs! I shot deep into him.

"Hypocrite!

Who wants to love
Without hate and
Without torture!
Is your tenderness more romantic than
A rose?
Or is your honey sweeter than
The bee's?
The rose slashes
The bee stings
That's the way things are

Don't speak to me of love as some
Ideal
Don't lecture to me of *amor* as an
Abstraction

Only the feeling matters

There aint no way to
Intellectualize or
Define or
Classify
The orange
Peeling it is it
Biting into it is it
Orange juice squirting is it
You taste it and
That is it
Sweet and sour
There is nothing complicated about
The orange
About anything
There is nothing perfect about
Amor

If you want the feeling
You gotta accept it in its
Entirety

It can't be separated into what it
Can never be

Unless
Can it be?
Your love is
Greater than
God's?

Fool!
Do you understand
Do you feel how
Vain
You are?'"

The veins in my neck were about to burst. Got no time for bullshit.

My baby Santo, no longer a baby, smiled, hugged me, cried and
collapsed. *Neta* is the best I could ever do. I noticed after that talk, he
tattooed a cross on his left hand, started really throwing himself into his art.
Skating around everywhere, keeping slim style. Graduated from Mission
High, started hitting City College, taking all them art classes, kicking it with
only positive people, like Alex, that Homey who works as a bouncer down at
that nightclub on San Bruno Avenue.

Now I bump into Toro limping on the street last Tuesday, and he tells
me that that little nigga Cartoon is back, but he says he aint Lil anymore.
Sweat smelling Toro told him that I had Santo's kid. Cartoon never knew
cause Lobo kicked him out before I got out of prison. Cartoon's gonna go
see Lobo in the pen. I already know what that means: trouble. Lobo's a shot
caller. Cartoon's a riot. They better not think about getting my baby involved
in their bullshit.

I laugh and stop myself.

That's just mama talkin. He's a big boy now, twenty years old in 2012,
even though he'll always be Lil Santo cause of his big pops. His blood is full
of love, so whatever he needs to do is straight with me. He's a good young
man, *amor* artist, still smells like cotton candy. Sometimes his Homey Alex
comes through, and they go touch up the old murals and help out painting the
new ones, like that sick ass gentrification mural on Balmy Alley, the one with

Alex's bad ass 72 Monte Carlo versus the cops. On top of the colorful mural you got the corrupt court system using technology to brutalize and displace the people most oppressed. A white skeleton in a judge's black robe types away the bullshit law on his laptop computer, and those fancy words trickle down to destroy *La Misión*. The orange and white 48 MUNI bus is running down 24th Street carrying around the brown wretched work folks, while the newbies get drunk off Starsucks lattes. The centerpiece is Alex's torch red 72 Monte and the Homeys controlling the streets. The cops are doing their dirt and harassing two youngsters, which is like the lil Homeys' rite of passage in the hood. Cops got to keep the streets clear of Brown and Black folks, so that the white folks feel nice and happy, safe. I know my baby Santo, even though he aint never been no gangbanger, cops still fuck with him, and they been fuckin with more kids more intensely now cause of this intense gentrification.

But a mama can't be trippin too much off what will or won't happen to her cub in the *varrio*, cause then I would just be plum fucking crazy.

Whatever he does, he does.

Aint gonna change my life anyhow. I'm just a janitor after all these years. Shit, gotta go to work in a few minutes. I clean houses and hotel rooms. After prison and trauma, what else can you hope for? I got flab all across my midsection. Varicose veins about to burst. Barely able to hang on livin in a little moldy apartment in the hood, even with my jobs. Still, I got no shame to my game.

I solve situations
That's what I do
You make the mess
I clean it up

Whatever you need
Front floors waxed
Bathroom scrubbed
The attic cleared of rats
The backyard's shrubs and
Roses pruned
A man murdered

You wanted to fly without wings
To touch unending sky

To play with the fire of sun
And now you find yourself here
A place you refuse to call destiny

Don't worry
I aint no prissy lady
I'm a janitor
I get my hands dirty and
Don't care about manners
I dig into shit no one else wants
That others refuse to acknowledge
Comes from themselves

I don't need your respect
I know the truth

Just pay me

CHAPTER FIVE — EL TORO

I wanted to kill someone. I wanted someone to kill me.

No military recruiter tried to conscript me or promise me anything beautiful like a GI Bill or a free funeral with burial plot. I did not know about those things. I knew the *Rambo* and *Commando* and *Full Metal Jacke*t propaganda and the street-gang respect the Marines held. I had to hunt for a recruiter who would even try to enlist me, as all the other recruiters laughed at me, dressed as a *cholo* with a long rap sheet. I had to leave. It was either the pen, death, insanity, or the Corps. I thought the Corps was the best option when I really had no options. At least I could be macho.

Twenty five years ago, within one week of my mama signing the contract for me, cause I was only 17, I was gone. I didn't tell anyone I was leaving. After I left, Brothers like Santo and Lobo, and some girls came searching for me, but moms told them I had joined the Marine Corps. I wanted it that way. I was too ashamed to tell people I was going to escape.

On November 9, 1987, at five o'clock in the black morning, I left my mother's house, walked to SFM's 24th Street BART, and headed to Oakland to be inducted in the Marines. Four years in the funk as a machine-gunner, I remember suffering a lot. Wanting to suffer and hating the suffering. Believing I deserved the suffering. Loving the suffering. Grunt gunner: M60 Echo Three and Mark 19 Grenade Gun. My weapons. My fists. My endurance and obedience to orders. My stupidity. Frontline. I came back home fucked up, but at least I knew the stupidity was mine, my choice, not a total brainwashing. I chose to do the stupidest shit by joining the Corps.

For thousands of years
We've questioned
Whether we actually have
Free Will
Or whether this is all just the
The illusion of acting

Did you action because you heard
In your head
Your mother?
Your school?
Church?

Peers?

What does it mean to
Freely Will
Something totally
On your own?

The answer is
Stupidity

You know you have
Free will
When on purpose
You do something
Stupid
Then you know
You aint no machine
Then you are really a
Human being
Not just a
Piano key
Being played

If you function
Purely out of
Logic
You are an algorithm
If you want to prove
Your humanity
Your Free Will
Throw yourself into
Stupidity

I joined, then fought in the war, the stupidest shit known to mankind.
Afterwards, it was a long road to recovery, rehabilitation. Back in 91 my legs
got shattered. Doc told me I'd never walk again, but how is a bull gonna be a
bull without the charge? I had to rise again, or I had to give it all up, and just
aint no way that a bull can surrender unless he's killed. So I looked for that:

death.

"Kill me motherfuckers. Do me a favor!" With all of my fury, I challenged the world.

But they pitied me more than they feared me. So I kept hobbling about, committing the sin of strength, as they kept underestimating me. Little by little, like a prisoner escaping by using a spoon to dig a tunnel, I made it back to the ring, but it wasn't just me that did it. There was something in me from way back I never knew, yet it was mine, too.

With originality
Rooted from spirit
We do not betray

Centuries ago
Our ancestors
Demanded from us
Something new
That they could
Never imagine

Then we were born

A true teacher
Requires his students to
One day
Kick his ass

It should be a
Proud moment
Without sadness or guilt
Without sin

Free
To insanity
And unknown new
Danger
The point of it all

I refined my charge in the Marines from 87-91, yeah, even suffered in the war, but I gets no love for that around here. Lots of dumb asses want to talk shit about the Corps, cause they think somehow I was a traitor for leaving the *varrio* for a bigger corruption, the United States. Brown man fighting for the white man, they think. Shit, I was only seventeen, yet I get blamed for all of the country's atrocities, but I understand cause I live in the radical revolutionary Mission, and some real and fake activists look at Marines as if they are *vendidos* to the hood cause they took off, and, yeah, maybe I was more than a bull to just get up and get out the *varrio*, but I wasn't no traitor. I was true, not privileged with any other alternative like school or a job, not privileged with some type of conscious politics. I was a *cholo* and met some other *cholo* Marines from all around that were grunts, too.

A gang of fuck-ups
Noble *locos*
Your option was
La Pinta
Or
The Green Machine

Both traditions loved you for
Your spirit of combat

You didn't analyze or evaluate
You just got shit done and
As long as you showed up
Groggy
Hungover
Half dead
Every morning at 5:00 o'clock
Ready to run and march and suffer
No matter what crimes you committed
The night before
Your sins would be forgiven

No one will ever understand
We had nothing
But we had each other

And that's all we needed
Por vida
Por muerte

The Corps purified the Toro in me. It didn't hit me back then, but I
wasn't the same as when I was a runt. I wasn't better than anyone else. The
war taught me that, but I sure wasn't the same old Toro that didn't think
at all. That's what the hugs and kisses, cheers, and hook ups were about.
Some people treated me like royalty. We were war heroes. We had kicked
ass, trampled the enemy oh so bad. The Highway of Death from Kuwait to
Iraq. Nope, we hadn't suffered too damn much, hadn't bled for our countries
like the fucking Iraqis. We were the winners by a rout. Killing, straight up,
no other word for what had happened over there. Killing is what made us
heroes. Half naked, starving men surrendering before us in the middle of a
smoky sand desert made us big shots. Violence, force, brutal power made
me a symbol of victory. But, damn, wasn't this the kind of shit I used to
do before the Corps? Wasn't this the same kind of mentality that had *gente*
locked up and getting executed?

Sure fucking was. Same fucking thing, no—worse. Worse or maybe,
actually, better cause I was different now. Different cause I knew how to
cause mass destruction—make people run and hide. Discipline gave me
that gift. Discipline is the instant willing obedience to orders, respect for
authority, and self-reliance, Sir. Had that drilled into me a million times over,
until it became a part of me.

It would become a part of the homeboys, too, cause I wasn't just gonna
leave them to die. I would incorporate my new theories about what a good
unit should be to the Homeys. I'd be a *vato loco* Marine, a solid street soldier.
Violence for the Corps made me accepted in all worlds. There was no other
way that I would have gotten that respect even with a million bucks, so it
would have to be violence that would get the *varrio* their proper respect.
Violence was the universal key. Violence and death is what good guys were
all about. With my experience and training, I would make sure we would be
the best.

The Best of Us Are the Most Fucked Up

You join to
Kill or

106

Be killed
To suffer
To laugh
The dream
First to fight
You pray for war
Imagining a
Banzai! Attack
Against you
Just for you
You in the middle of
Blood and Guts
Combat

You are a special
Target
A Marine
A grunt
Front line
The poorest of
The poor
The stupidest
Rock
Known to man
But contrary to popular
Belief
You are not more
Brainwashed
Than anyone else
You know life
You know death
It's your tradition

Belleau Wood
Iwo Jima
Khe Sanh
Beirut
Kuwait

Afghanistan
Iraq

You don't pick the war
You just show up and
They are there
Ready for you
To patrol the jungle
To jump into the trench
To step on the booby trap
To know nothing
Your dream come true

You are Ira Hayes
Un Indio
Un Pima Indio
Who lifted
UP
And planted
The American Flag on
Mount Suribachi
The iconic
Image of the 20th century

The *Indio*
Against
The Samurai
The *Indio* won
But that victory
Led to his
Death in a ditch
Back at home
An Arizona Injun Reservation
A giant concentration camp
Ira Hayes did not want to be a
Hero
For
Genocide

He came back to the
Rez and
Drank
Fire water
Would get arrested
Thrown in the can
Get up
Get out
Then do it all over
Again

A good Marine
A jughead
A gyrene
High and Tight
Devil Dog

You act like it
Aint shit
Tough
Cool
Crazy
Everybody knows
That shit has
Consequences

Death in a ditch

You're a
Marine
Ira Hayes
The best of us
The most fucked
UP

They gave me medals for being in a nightmare.
Once I got back to *La Misión* in 91, the Homeys that were real street

Homeys, like Lobo, Santo, and even Lil Toon, they knew I had talent, mad skills for our fight, which was always fast forward in the worst wars, whether that's in the desert of Saudi Arabia, the streets of *La Misión*, or the cell blocks in Pelican Bay *Pinta*. Even though I hadn't gotten swept up in the mass incarceration system like hella other Homeys, I had my respect as a fighter, especially because on the streets I would still just take off my shirt and put up my dukes at the drop of a dime. Packed a nine mil or a .380, too, but never let that do the work for me when I knew the right thing to do was be a bare-knuckle brawler. No matter where you are, the frontline is the frontline if you make it the frontline. All the Homeys knew it was our duty to make everywhere we went the frontline. I was still young, but I was becoming an O.G., through the spirit of all O.G.'s who keep the cycle going.

Full force fast forward
Beyond the speed of light
Original Gangster
Original Genius

You cracked the code that
The schoolbooks
Streets
Prisons
Educational institutions
Television sets and
Mickey Mouse (ABC) news programs
Were all a hoax

With their mild mannered Midwestern voices
Nice newscasters
Program people into believing that there is
Truth
And that they know what it is
That they got the market on the motherfucker
They know what's good for you
Good for sheep

Original Genius
Todo Bodo Down

Everyone else played the fool
Buying into weasel words
And far out fantasies like
Justice
But you played it cool
Experimenting
Hustling
Inventing on your own
Your own identity
Beyond the theory of relativity

When they look back at this time
100 years from now
They'll see it was you who was
Smarter than Shakespeare
And like his plays and poems
You will be recreated thousands of times over

Your graffiti on the wall
Your prison letters
Your poetry of life
Of lowrider *locura*
Were the purest mutinies of the mind
The Original Genius
Revolutionary of cockroach class

Coming back was coming down. Constant ringing in my ears that I couldn't escape. I had seen mass destruction at the international war level: thousands of tanks ramming toe-to-toe against each other, hundreds of oil wells burning their poison through the sky and blacking out the sun, tremors, chemical attacks, pissing on yourself, praying to God, breaching the explosion mine fields, assaulting the trenches, imagining World War One all over again. Most of the time, we can't do shit but just sit and be scared, trapped, confined in a makeshift tin beer can vehicle until they call down orders for us, the grunts. It's a tank fight mostly, so we, frontline Marines, wait for hand-to-hand combat, anticipating the worst. All around, you hear the deafening thunder of hell on earth calling you to death. Coming back from that shit, I was fucked up, guilty to be grateful, but played it off. You just don't know how all that trauma hurts you, and whether you can even admit that it hurts you, so my best solution to this unknown feeling, this horror, was strong drink and solid streets. Many a morning I'd find myself laid out on the sidewalk.

Hungover
Crudo
22 years young
On pretty sunny
Sunday mornings
I loved to
Hike from
Cortland Avenue
Up to history
A place of peace
The old boarded-up liquor store on
Eugenia and Wool Street
Where I would dream on a
Beautiful bed of cement

I lie on the sidewalk
Because it offers truth
The mattress of wisdom is
So snug
Better than a hunk of down feathers
Cold road
Exactly what you need for
Drunk bones
On fire from firewater

The dream is about all that poison
Draining out of your body
Onto the cold concrete
It's good
The best dream
No better goal in the universe
But to sleep without your shirt
On Eugenia Street

Next to the old
Wool Street Grocery sign
Memories
Pure medicine
Black tar
Gray crazy days
Just like the *loco*
Concrete
Full of cracks
Potholes
Shattered glass

When I was 15
In 1985
We would stroll into that store
When it existed and
I would count pennies at the register

One, two, three…

And the Black store clerk would study me
Counting copper
While the Homeys
At the freezers
Filled up free forties
Into backpacks

Twenty one, twenty two, twenty three…

When they jammed out
Sometimes with stuttered chuckles
I was done, too, and snatched my paid-for
Pack of gum
So that afterwards we wouldn't stink like
Olde English Malt Liquor
Like Shakespeare

"To die, to sleep –

To sleep, perchance to dream –
Ay, there's the rub,
For in this sleep of death
What dreams may come"

Yesterday, yesterday
When I was young

I wake
It's almost noon
Sunday morning
Coming down

Had to get out of that rut. Couldn't depend on the Marines or the Homeys or even myself. I needed to go outside of myself with some bullshit abstractions, goals and more than goals, like in the Corps we call it Mission Accomplishment. And even if we aint got a mission, we invent missions, like constantly field daying, which is toothbrush cleaning the fuck out of everything. Like PT—physical training, which I still do, calisthenics, weights, power explosions everywhere I go. I'm thickness, solid muscle. But I gave up my own authority to Lobo for the big plans, what we needed to do, cause that motherfucker had big brain wolf skills, always plotting, taking risks, calculating with street sense before going in for the kill.

He's the one who called the shot after Santo sacrificed himself for us, that we had to push out Cartoon for his own good, for our own good, that we needed to have bigger plans, extended plans, more than just robbing and stealing and dealing poison and being traumatized and killed. It was me having gone to the Marines that gave Lobo the idea that Cartoon needed to get the fuck out, venture out on his own, but without being dragged down by war. We pinned all our hopes on Toon. He was about five years younger than us, still a juvenile, but he had good game, the best learned from us and the streets. Lobo and I both felt Little Cartoon could do it, knew he was from good stock, that he would one day return, even though now, fuckin Lobo is gone for life at Quentin.

And now what about all those big goals, taking over the world? Shit, once Lobo got busted a dozen years ago, back in 2000, there was really no one else left. I reverted back to my Toro essence, started fighting in the ring again. And it wasn't for no illusory goals of becoming champion of the world. After all these years and scars, I understand all shitty goals are a big cover up that we believe can actually help us see, but it aint nowhere except in our minds, even that final goal. Maybe I'm obsessed with death.

REDRUM

In order to be successful
They say you gotta have not only
Goals but also
Vision

My life vision is death

My life vision is a life that is alive
Through the search for death
In that life that is hunting
There is vision

We are all in the same
Life and death
That is the only truth
Therefore there is only
The moment
Yet the moment keeps escaping us
Even though it is
Now!

Perpetual war
Front line combat
Against the only thing that
Is
Which is
You

We do not share the
Is
You live your life
I live mine

Our sense of
Is
Can only be
Ours
Regardless of any
Empathy or
Envy

The vision can attempt love
Which is also a life that is alive
But even
Darling love
Must search for death through life
This cycle

A lowrider bi-cycle
Chrome wheels spinning
Round and round
Glittering twisted forks
Steering you to
Comedy and tragedy
You ride and feel the wind
A wise whisper
A sweet remembrance
That simply moves
You pedaled it to happen by
Constantly forcing forward

Then
BLAM
You are hit by a
A lowrider car
The infamous
1972 Chevy Monte Carlo
REDRUM
REDRUM

It does not stop

The only one who knows about death is the one who can no longer tell us about it. Sick Santo knows. He's out there. You get the magic only once you go. Thinking about it aint a fascination or obsession with death. It's just the thing that keeps you humble and understanding.

But, man, maybe there is hope, too.

Cartoon is back. After twenty years and with no real reason to come back, that fool is back, and maybe in 2012 there can be something more. I don't know—a takeover, more gangsters, more *locos*, maybe even success, whatever the hell that means. He's gonna go see Lobo. They're both smart, both down as fuck. Smarter and downer than any of these fucking politicians or programs they got for us. They're the streets, *la gente*, rooted in *amor*. They'll get some shit moving, and we'll get better. As long as I got this life, I move til I got it no more.

Hasta muerte
Vivo
Until death
I live

I will not just exist
Like some make-believe
Word
I will punch out of this
Life
This
Word

I've been dead while
Alive
I do not like it
Even though
Not liking it means
Nothing

I do it anyway
Beyond the words
This thing called
Life

117

Which revolves around
Another make-believe
Thing that not even
Dogs
Care about:
Time

I am in it but
Not in it
Invisible and untouchable
Yet there
The most powerful thing
I can imagine
The moment
And
With this moment
I wrestle
Rising
Falling
Feeling
All

I cannot desire more because
There is
Nothing else

Hasta muerte
Vivo
Until death
I live in
The moment

The moment is sincerity. The moment is beauty, like a red rose. That's why I love to fight so much cause I am right smack in the middle of the moment, but at forty-two fucking years old now, I got to always be ready to get knocked the fuck out. Getting knocked out, too, is the moment.

I saw Maricela, that knockout, that red rose, the other day. I told her that Cartoon was back. She set down her two bags of groceries in the middle of

Treat Street so we could talk more. I thought of Lil Santo, her son, Santo's son. I have a feeling Lil Santo is gonna get with it. I've kept him away on purpose cause I haven't had any ideas to give him, and I aint wanted him to live my life of violence.

"I hope they don't think they're gonna get my baby involved in their shit." Maricela, too, was the bull, someone who loved and thrived in war. She smiled with her Newport cigarette dangling from her lip.

"We're the last ones, Mari. You know Santo loved this *varrio*, gave his life for it." I reminded her, but she didn't need reminding.

"Fool, who you tryin to school?" Maricela maddogged me harder than a man. She smelled of cheap perfume and bloody guts. "Whatever Lil Santo does, he does. He got a good head, a pure heart. Of course, he's a lil *loco*, too, but he keeps solid company. Hangs around with Alex Neta, you know, that lowrider youngster with the red 72, and Lil Santo even goes to City College." Maricela was proud.

"Yeah, Lil Santo and Alex Neta, that's the new generation of homeboys, but we're still the minority, or at least that's what these hipsters are trying to make us feel. These new motherfuckers that look at me like if I'm shit."

"Yeah," Maricela agreed, "but the hipsters can't really harm you; it's their muscle I trip off, the fucking cops. Man, they been pressing the youngsters hard. Always jamming them up for just walking down the streets. That gang injunction law was just an excuse to keep all Homeys off the streets and set up a military-like occupation zone, like the one they got in Iraq. I sometimes get worried for Lil Santo." Tough Maricela showed she was a good conscious mama.

"It's an upside down world where the police that promise to protect you are actually there to destroy you." I wanted to comfort her but knew only how to tell the truth. "I love and respect my enemies, as long as they keep it real, but they don't, so I tell em.

Don't approach me with a smile
Raise up your knife
Show it to the sky
If stabbing is what you intend to do

I am more disgusted by
The mystery
Than

Sincerity
Murder being
The most sincere of
Arts

When you shank me
Look me in the face
Know what you are doing
I will try not to hold it against you
I will try to be graceful
In my own death

What else can one do
Except expect
A rose?"

The rose can't exist without first the dirt. I hugged Maricela, wanted to kiss her, that red rose that has lots of dirt on her, but the dirt's exactly what makes all flowers beautiful. She sashayed away, and I knew she was solid. The dirt is the frontline, a line that is all fucked up and uneven, exactly as it should be.

Straight lines were made to be smashed
Nice and neat
Snorted up the nose
Little bit left over as powder
Make up
For a pretty face
Not mine

Been stumbling around my whole life
The crooked line is
A maze
I put up my dukes
Punch out in every direction
Don't matter I hit air or
The bus
Keep swingin

Cause I'm El Toro
Eventually I'll get to
The front
Where they tell me there's some type of
Illumination

I don't know

I believe
Black eyes
Busted teeth
Cuts on knuckles
Swollen lips
Holes in the head
Proof of
Transcendence

Medals don't mean nothin
Down in the trenches

Always felt and knew the Mission was front line in so many ways, the front line of *locos* and *loca*s, the front line of creativity, the front line of power.

New hipsters aint no joke. We got used to white boys being punks in our tough public schools and jails, but that's just here in the *varrio*, in Frisco. Man, down in Alabama they got white pride like a motherfucker. They are getting bolder and want to take back the inner-city land they gave up some decades ago in this make-believe white flight bullshit. They're going through an identity crisis, and we are the ones to blame; anyone that looks Mexican stole their job from them.

I feel it. And the cops feel more for the privileged than they do for us, the fucking targets of all this insanity, including gentrification, mass incarceration, and extra judicial assassinations. Cause these cops are on a mission. They train the fucking rookies right here on 24th Street and throughout the Mission backstreets. Shit, last week, I saw a buffed ass rookie with a loaded shotgun runnin through the hood hunting for this frail ass homeless tweaker! As if that buffed cop couldn't just tackle that homeless Homey! It's all meant to be an intimidation, and like Maricela said, a military occupation. It aint no coincidence that the gang injunctions are targeted here in *La Misión*. Man, that shit is just an excuse to erase us and keep our brown skin out of sight so that the newbies aint gotta feel threatened. Convinced even lots of our own people that we're the bad guys when we're really just patsies of the system.

Yeah, we used to mob em, the hipsters, still do from time to time, but they got some power. Comin from Arkansas and Tennessee. Think they know some things. Manifest Destiny, they believe that shit.

But the schools and their textbooks don't teach em: we resisted. We fought. That is the only reason why and how we are still alive. By grasping this, we stay ready. Fighting keeps us ready. That's all I do—built a reputation as a heavy hitter with a solid left hook, taking on all comers right there at the stadium on 25th and Capp. I was becoming a mark, but I didn't give a fuck. Some Whites wanted to do more than fight me, cause I was more than just dangerous with my fists. I got dangerous spirit.

I aint paranoid
Only conscious
Which is worse
I have read and lived
Enough history
To predict
Our future:
War

Knowing who I am
The tall
Skinny
Skinhead
Hiked up to me
At the top of
Mission Dolores Park
Targeting me as his
Brown Bullseye

I stood straight
But also
Ignored him

Played it cool
Because
Que sera
Sera

When he got within earshot
I maddogged him
Let him have it
Just like a good
Machinegunner should
"I was in the Marine Corps"
It was not a threat or vanity or disability
Simply a fact
Which meant
His shaved head
His black combat boots
Could never compare
To mine
In spitting that at him
I let him know
I am more American
Than he could ever be
A frontline
Combat action
Grunt

I have no other place
To go to
Except
Forward

"Fuck Nazis" I declared

"What?" He whimpered

How could a lil injun be so bold?

"Fuck Nazis

All enemies foreign and domestic"
I showed him no mercy
As my enemy
Has never shown me mercy

I remember fighting the good fight
At sixteen years old
But being stomped
Stabbed in the head
Kicked in the mouth
By three hillbillys on top of me
In the middle of the street
Having to pretend I was dead
In order for them to quit
No mercy
Once they left and I staggered up
I was proud of blood showering down
The front of my face
Later I collapsed at the hospital
Was knocked out for a couple of days

Never underestimate your enemy

This young white man
At *La Misión de Dolores Parque*
Was some sort of hitter
Had done some research
Come to test me
El Toro
Challenge me
Perhaps
Kill me

"What are you doing up here?"
He asked innocently

"I'm looking for a fight"
I could jump on top of him

Flip him around
Clamp onto his neck
Never let it go

"Oh, yeah?"
He had
Pretty blue eyes
Clean face
Rotten teeth

He knew exactly what this was
Who he was
Who I was
New racists are clever
Think they can get into some sort of
Weasel words
Exchange
Explanation
Conversation
Pacification

"Either you're here to
Kill or
Be killed
I got nothing more to say to you"
I said

During an attack
Never let your guard down
Never confess to the cops

"Ok"
He said sadly
"See you later"
He bounced back down the green grass

There is no later
I see him all the time

Everywhere I go
I aint paranoid
Only conscious

I stay ready

    This aint no rare phenomenon in the most liberal place on Planet Earth, San Francisco. These types of ordeals are becoming the standard. You got bold racists getting bolder, and meek mice getting sneakier, calling the cops on us, using snitch technology apps to bust up crowds of Latinos more than four deep.

    I don't know if there is any such thing as a solution at this stage, but I know aint no better brains than Lobo and Cartoon to make magic. I'm anxious for them to start some shit. Maybe violence. Maybe organization. Maybe revolution. I don't know. I defer to them, cause I know what I do, and that is the charge. No matter how old I get, I stay at the front. I got trust. I got loyalty, what you might call stupidity, but what I think is *Neta*. Cause aint gonna be no politicians or school teachers or saviors out of the sky that are gonna come and give us love. It's always been up to us, our own selves, for that. It aint gotta be a total overthrow for it to be success. Our survival alone is success. Every moment being different than them is success. Every moment with dignity and style is accomplishment. Every moment charging forward fighting is victory.

    I know who I am, El Toro.

I am brown like shit
That fertilizes flowers and food
I am brown like dirt
That sustains skyscrapers and *sueños*
Brown hot coffee
Fuel for faceless forms
Inspiration for tired troops

Your victim
Back broken coffee picking
Slave
Happy--

Because what else is there
When you have nothing
But muscles and brown skin?

On *Cinco de Mayo*,
I down Corona beer
And get drunk like a Mexican
Even though
My parents were from Guatemala

It doesn't matter
We are all brown pieces of shit
Who share suffering and smiles
Heartbreaks and heaven
We know how to live
And how to die

Con Safos, Homes

CHAPTER SIX —
CARTOON VISITS LOBO AT SAN QUENTIN PINTA

In his sharp prison blues uniform, Lobo sat on a steel stool, breathed into the prison phone, and looked past the bullet proof glass at Cartoon, who was no longer a runt, but a tough full-fledged man, a Homeboy who understood the look of death. Lobo had imagined this conversation twenty years earlier when he kicked Cartoon out and predicted one day he would return. Now in 2012 there was no need for explanations or apologies, no need for salutations. Slim and fit Lobo smiled and started spitting.

"The future funk is not yet defined, but corruption started it all off and aint going nowhere, no matter how evolved we pretend to be. Shit, evolution makes us worse!" Lobo scratched at the fleas in his crotch. "If you aint got the guts to first and foremost and constantly admit that this world is rooted in inconsistency and dishonesty, depravity and perversion, then, motherfucker, we can't even have an intelligent conversation, so excuse me while I kick it in this corner and play dumb dunce, a camouflaged guerilla,

The ultimate gangster

An American icon
A rebel
Undercover but
Honest even in deception
One goal is all that matters:

Familia

Not the corruption of the gang
But real family in its finest form
Children
Future
Amor

The gangster knows the sham
And doesn't try to fix what can't be fixed
Practical
Realistic

He knows you must steal your bread
He knows you must hustle your life

The good things are not sins
Wine and whiskey
Laughter
Lust
Freedom
But the freedom for what?

To live life the way he wants

Like the guerilla
Camouflaged
The gangster fights his battles in darkness
He believes in honor
Accepts deception and death
Without crying

For thirty five years
Vincent 'The Chin'
Genovese Family
Godfather
In pajamas
Bathrobe and
Slippers
Tottered through
The New York streets and
Federal prisons
Feigning insanity
Keeping it all together

The Boss.

You were that future I saw twenty years ago." Lobo needed to let out
his heart, did not want to hear even one word from Cartoon, and Cartoon
suited and booted in a charcoal suit and maroon tie, simply shut up, nodded
his head, and listened to wisdom, exactly as Santo the Spirit had urged him to

listen. "You were the *familia* that I never had growing up. It's the best echo of a dream. Now after having hella kids that don't visit me and that I aint never gonna see again and being locked up so many fucking years, I wish for that only thing that seems to have any real meaning: *familia*." Lobo had aged. Unlike the Wolfman, Lobo was bald. His dark brown head was shiny. He brandished a thick salt and pepper goatee. Cartoon patted his slick-backed hair and nodded to Lobo, who smiled his broken tooth smile.

"Fuck it. You're my family, Cartoon, cause you came back after twenty years, you funny gangsta. You made it." Lobo tried not to choke. "The *carnal*es in here are my family, too." Lobo chuckled with a broken heart.

Cartoon's black and silver watch suddenly felt tight on his wrist, but he held the phone firmly. "Yes, Brother, I am your family," he said. "If I made anything, it was so I could give it all back to you, you who saved my life."

"And the beat goes on." Lobo beamed. "You aint little anymore. You're a bona-fide OG, but even more than that. *Barrio Bushido*." Lobo's eyes looked back to the past, looked forward into the future. "One day they'll look back at us OG's with nostalgia, a burning desire for the past, like what the Japanese had for the samurais, their *Bushido*, but it aint no going back, never." Lobo had learned a lot. Dozens of books a week. Reading Dostoevsky, Pessoa, Hong-Kingston, Garcia-Marquez, y mas. Unlike the stupid convicts that the media portrayed them to be, Lobo was wily and smart, slick and sour, a real *loco*. His *familia* inside these walls mandated every homeboy to read and become educated, to write essays and to report promptly when ordered. Disciplined, strong, always hitting *machina*, a strict military-like physical fitness regimen of burpees, pushups, pullups, squats. Their prison gang system was both worse and better than the best, like Berkeley, Oxford, Harvard, Davis, Disneyland.

"The samurais, though, couldn't handle the new capitalist world," Lobo continued. "I mean what the fuck good is swinging a sword when you got to create quarterly profits?" Lobo sneered. "That's why their own country got rid of em. Capitalism beat out tradition. This wicked world is beyond that monster. It's

Ahh-Mehr-EEE-Kah
With a Spanish accent
About a lost explorer
Amerigo Vespuchi
Who discovered nothing

But at least got it right that this place was not
China

My country tis of thee
Sweet land of liberty
Treacherous mountains
Soothing snow
Hell heat
Chicago wind
Fog along the Frisco bay
The Tennessee Waltz
New York salsa
Kansas City royalty
Denver tough guys
Oakland jungles

We got it all
McDonald's golden arches
Big Mac hamburgers
Full-time obesity and strangling varicose veins
A talented athlete who can stuff down his throat
72 hot dogs in ten minutes
Lowrider cars cruising down pot-holed streets
Hobos hunting through garbage cans for aluminum gold
I-phones and apps and assholes
Brown men washing dishes
Black women strutting down the street
White girls with diamond smiles
Rednecks with red anger
Chinese folks practicing the deadly art of Tai Chi in green parks
Indians with green cards landing top notch jobs in Silicon Valley
Indians on reservations drinking too much smoking too much
Dying too much

The Statue of Liberty
Aint got on any underwear
Underneath that gown
Always ready to fuck

Her torch is lit but it aint for light
It's for burning shit down

Resist
Conform
It's the same damn thing
Cook the meth
Eat your broccoli
Snort the Coke
The famous 70's Coca Cola slogan
It's the real thing
What the world wants today:

Capitalism
The birth of a nation

And we all eat it up
Our own baby
This shit sandwich
This imperfect existence where
Little old ladies love driving their big old Cadillacs
But they aint gonna take that Middle East machine-gun nest
For some gasoline
Which means that
We're all to blame and question in the biggest wars ever fought and
Those biggest wars that we've always won
Lest we forget who we are
Lest we play ignorant about what this all means
Humanity goes out the window
Cause we all need more spaceships and
Rocket fuel and more chips and speed

America
You are my bitch
America
You are my reflection in the mirror
America
You are capable of anything

Murder and mayhem
War and destruction
Love and tenderness
I pray that your
Holy hills
Bless us
Keep us
Safeguard us from ourselves
America
You trick me and get me stoned
Supercharging your smoke
Into my cancered lungs
America
You break my heart into 1776 pieces
Yet
Still
I love you

A true patriot
Looks you in the face
When they lie and tell you
The tragic truth

And aint I a patriot who off my back built this country?" Lobo wanted
to stand up from the stool but the short wire cord connected to both the phone
and wall would not allow him to do anything but sit. "Aint I the nostalgia
America loves? Shit, cause even capitalism, though it may be the root and
also what they want now, it aint what the future is." Lobo looked at the
plain white visiting room, nodded at the Big Brother cameras in the corner.
"It's surveillance, Homes, it's Data-ism. Fuck Orwell's 1984—this shit is
way crazier than that," Lobo said, and Cartoon concurred, absorbing all of
the information, understanding even more than Lobo because Cartoon was
actually living on the outside and witnessing the digital transformation for
himself, through others who were glued to technology. "But check out,"
Lobo leaned into the phone, "What America really loves, beyond anything
else is a *loco*, a frontiersman, a rascal ass Lobo, a wolf not of Wall Street,
but the wolf of war." Lobo sat as level as possible and pierced directly into
Cartoon.

"I understand, I agree, Bro," Cartoon said looking into Lobo. "History gots no Homeys, only enemies."

"Yeah, I can maddog you and rush you without a word," Lobo's voice stayed steady. "Cause here in *la pinta* we have perfected the art that all aspire to, look you up and down, size you up and just do it: your life, Homes, cause it don't matter if I win or you win. I win as long as I'm causing damage, hurt, and pain."

"But Brother," Cartoon knew he, too, was supposed to have been behind the other side of the bullet proof glass, "Don't you feel used like a pawn?" Cartoon had to engage, because he, too, had read many books and thought about this matter deeply in all the years he had been away.

"Of course, I'm a fucking pawn." Lobo was upset at the stupid question that required him to confess the stupid answer. "I'm the capital for one of the most profitable money making institutions in modern history: the prisons. Man, before they had *gente* pickin cotton or coffee or lettuce, but now they don't even need our muscles, Homes! They just throw us in these cages where we play dominoes and spades while they cash in on our spirits. My actual body is their capital, their profit. I feed the guards, lawyers, and judges' children and educate them through college, so they can then become the lawyers that lock all of our asses up!" Lobo laughed, his brown bald head glistening with sweat. "Come on, man, the California prison guard union is the strongest prison union in the world. They aint here to guard us from society; they're here to protect their investment: me." With his slender fingers, Lobo rubbed his long goatee like a wise kung fu master. "And what the fuck is my reward for all my hard work that pays all these other motherfuckers' bills?

Life.

Life in *La Pinta*. This is my reward for being a good rebellious wolf: Life."

"How can you take it?" Cartoon asked. Although he had done some petty time here and there in scattered cities, at least he had gone on a journey that allowed him freedom of movement.

"I read. I jack off, but not too much cause you get weak," Lobo said it as a matter of fact. "I take classes here. They got U.C. Berkeley nearby here so we get lots of nice white volunteer teachers. Shit, one of my favorite, most torturous games in my cell is I play back in my mind all the women I loved, all the women who loved and hated me, El *Loco* Lobo. I remember their strong thighs, their soft navels, their hypnotic eyes. I took an English class in here, like if I don't already know fucking English, and they would get us used to writing by giving us exercises for creativity. Writing makes you remember." Lobo looked into the beyond.

"To be a good writer
The teachers tell you to
Read more
Learn plot
Describe the weather
Master grammar
Lull them to sleep

They tell you that
There are exercises
That can work your creative
Muscles
Describe a first

Your first kitten
Your first day of school
Your first kiss

My first fuck
I had never known her
Never seen her
But my Homey told me
There's this girl
She fucks anyone
I was anyone
No one
Thirteen years old
Scared
Excited
With a boner
Ready to pop

We rendezvoused behind the schoolhouse
She showed up

Fat
Greasy
Grotesque
Ready for love

Cold Frisco morning
In the basement of an abandoned house
On Excelsior Street
A wooden plank as our bed
I pulled down my pants
So did she
We fucked with our shirts and jackets still on
I didn't kiss her
She didn't kiss me
We didn't speak
I came
I don't know what she got
We lay there
Without speaking
We put our pants on to keep warm
We took them off
To fuck again
We crawled out from underneath our
Love nest
Flew our separate ways

A few days later
I received her gift
Felt the tingling in my groin
Opened up her love letter
Delivered underneath my underwear
They were like micro
Chocolate chips
Clutching onto me
And once plucked out
Scurried around
Searching, too, for
Love

Little crabs
Our love children

I can't remember her name
Never saw her again but
I will remember her for
The rest of my life
My first."

Lobo in a daze looked upwards.

"You got creative, Brother. I learned along the way a good writer is supposed to hit you on the head, and you, the reader, are supposed to say thank you for the lump! You hit my head, Homes." Cartoon grinned a writer's grin. "You learned to keep yourself busy and protect yourself against the demons."

"Fuck all of this, Cartoon," Lobo retorted. "The best protection from the total insanity was always a woman. Fuck these books for a good ass woman! And the best kind of woman is a woman in love," Lobo stated *Neta*. "Love, this foundation, spread out to other things, lots of good things. We had love, Brother, for so much in the worst of places. We had love and laughter, our secret to life. And if you wanted that love, there was a real good selfishness needed. Selflessness, too, actually. Cause when you love, it aint no longer about just you. You want your other to be loved more than you are loved. In doing that, you are also loved beyond your heart." Lobo was almost singing it. Cartoon's smooth shaven face beamed brightly. "That's community, Brother. Shit, the ideal of the gangs, too, but everything gets corrupted. That's why like I said earlier, you can only look for proof in the real people you can see, hear, smell, taste, and touch, *familia*.

I'm telling you about love, real romance, the key to hunting! You need to be romantic, Homes. That's the key to the kingdom; aint writing alone. Writing springs from romance, and then romance springs back into the writing.

Sheila

"Sheila, she was my girl." Lobo's eyes watered.

"I remember her." Cartoon gave no reaction, would not insult Lobo's pain by giving him some type of weak empathy or bullshit emotions that could never do justice to the love of Lobo's life.

"So many years later, I'm still haunted by her love." Lobo's eyes glazed over as he looked down. "I remember the first day we met.

It was a beautiful blue day
April 1991
At the beach
Snuggling together
With the ocean smashing
Towards us

I love you
Was the stupidest thing
She could say to a
Fool like me

She ruined it
No appreciation of the moment
The fairytale of forever was necessary
Idiot I accepted the challenge

So you love
A *loco*
A Lobo
Who drunk will sing outside your window
At four o'clock in the morning
When even decent gray fat rats are sleeping in peace
Who will write you poems of pretty pettiness and
Piss off your parents and relations
Who will never surrender to common sense or reason
Searching through trash for truth
Who you will pray for and damn during the same session
Not knowing and afraid to know whether
God holds the power
To make him different than he is
To make him better or at least
Normal

He aint never gonna change

I told Sheila

I will be worthy of your love and
Unfortunately
You aint gonna like it
You will suffer and
So will I
But that's the way you want it
With your fucking love

I will not let you down.

    I sold her out," Lobo told the truth, and the truth did not save him.
"Tricked her, made her love me, then threw her away. It was cause of me she
was murdered, and I could have saved her but didn't. I loved gold more than
Sheila. And I played it off, still do, that I'm some kind of tough guy, but that
aint real. I cry the tears of a clown." Lobo tilted up his chin with fake pride.
He spoke to her.

"It's funny
Not in the ha ha sense
Of course
But it's funny
That all those years on the streets
I never dreamed of you
Sheila

My dreams
My imagination
Were all lies
Infidelities
Even unto myself
My dreams represented
An infant's desire
An idiot's pettiness
A grown man's evil
Clichés of a life
That was supposed to be

Corrupted by
Lust
Gluttony
Machismo

Then there was you
And maybe
I initially thought it would be the same
But the way you laughed and looked
Without makeup
The way you wrote and shared
Simplicity
The way you moved like a
Pantheress
The way
The only way you proved
Love
I knew something had changed

I had you
You were mine
I lost you
You were gone
The only thing left were dreams

Dreams alive
With truth
A clown ghost
That haunts me
Both in and out of
Consciousness

It's funny
Not in the ha ha sense
Of course
But it's funny
That I never dreamed of you
Til you were dead."

Lobo stopped, and there was silence.

Both of them sat still, looked to the periphery of each other, did not dare make eye contact. Then after enough emptiness had passed, time dissolved the feeling. Lobo had released his burden.

"Back in the 80's and 90's I used to call em all bitches," Lobo said. "Used to try to protect myself with machismo. These years make me reflect. You know, we didn't even know how we were being programmed by the mass media, gangsta rap, sick shit, yeah, some reality, too, but most of it was fronting. I never really believed in my heart any woman was a bitch. I just couldn't never expose my heart, and I knew our lifestyle was sending us to death or right here, *La Pinta*. Shit, falling in love and showing your heart was weakness, cause how the hell are you supposed to survive in here and show your heart, be all in love? You'll get got." Lobo slapped himself in the face. "Now all I got are these worn out teeth and wiry muscles, and they don't help my heart." He was hurt.

"War is the only cure for unbearable pain," Lobo said in sorrow. Cartoon looked down. "In war the only goals are reward or destruction. Yeah, I made it for a minute on the streets, was a hood star, driving it all, a Mercedes, Beemer, and lowrider, wearing sharkskin suits, howling at lots of hurt. But it wasn't no reward. Was just goal gettin.

Vanity
Confusion
Desperation
Reaching for
Nothing

If we start with
Ignorance
We can have fun
Goal gettin

If we start with
Knowledge of our
Absurdity
We can also have fun
Goal gettin

The ignorant exist
In their ignorance
Same as
The wise also
Only exist
In their wisdom
One aint better than the other
Existence is existence
It's the same thing

A dead wise man aint no
Better
Than a live fool
The idiot at least exists
While the dead
Know only death
Which means nothing to the
Living

We need some illusions
Some carrot or
Prize
To help us escape
The impossible
Nothing
That is our shared fate

So get your goal
Make it yours
Have a good time
Reaching for
Nothing or
Something
Whatever
Chase that carrot and
Bounce bunny!
Be fulfilled
Get your goal

Your waste of time and
Then
Invent all over again."

Lobo grinned at Cartoon, laughed at himself.

"I knew the statistics. I knew I was supposed to get busted, and I did.
Smile Now, Cry Later, Homes." Lobo showed the scars and tattoos on his
fists. "War in *La Pinta* is paranoia, constant attacks even in my nightmares.
And this is what I get, lots of good suffering to mask the suffering connected
to the love of my life, Sheila, who I sold out for less substance than thirty
pieces of silver. Judas, the wolf.

Now I'm gettin old, maybe sentimental, but I've discovered nothin
outside really changes.

It's Only You Who Changes

Wasted time is the worst
You clutch to hope
That will never come

Time does not stop or forgive
Or cry or care
For your petty possibilities
Its answer is always death

You keep on trying to figure it out
Without realizing that the racket
Blasting in your brain
Is time's silent persecution
You are a victim
And there's nothing you can do about it

Your time is gone
Like her ruby red lipstick washed off your collar
You do not even deserve something to remember her by
The laundry detergent
Too powerful
Too clean

For your soiled plans and parties

Wasted time is
The only alternative
We live for our illusions
Falling down drunk
Flying free
Prudish purpose
The same shit
The same shit

Time is time
The best of times
The worst of times
Is the same shit

It's only you who changes
Someone
Something
Different
More powerful
Less petty
Than eternity

And now what, Cartoon?!" Lobo twisted quickly, flaunting his
remaining sharp brown and white teeth.

Although Cartoon had traveled a lot, he had stayed mostly in cities like
Chicago, St. Louis, Cleveland, Queens. He had not spent time in the ice-land
forests of Minnesota or behind the walls of Q, where the wolves howled and
killed the most. Cartoon simply did not know how to answer.

"Am I supposed to feel sorry for myself?" Lobo asked. "Shit, don't no
one got time for that noise. I pity no one, not even myself, and hell no, not
you. In Between My Fingers, I'm Playin The World's Smallest Violin Just for
You.

There is a great loss in
No longer
Being able to be

Sad

The loss comes when you finally
Admit
You are the one to blame
Guilty as charged

Not by any justice
Not by any wisdom
Not by any nothing

But you
Only you
You are a piece of shit
The world would be a better place
Without you

That is liberation
Because you realize
The world
Is only you

We are all our own worlds
Maybe we're connected in the cosmos of
Outer space
But you live with you
They live with themselves

The world cannot be a better place
Without you
Because the word
World
Is meaningless
Without you in it

We travel on

So there is a great sadness

In knowing that
Sadness is also a lie
A journey
That ultimately
Ends."

Lobo sighed, smiled. "All this talk of war and sadness gets me bored, cause that shit is old news." He was ready for something new, original. "So what we gonna do?" Lobo was ready to explode.

"Brother Wolf," Cartoon said it calmly, as if he were Saint Francis, San Fran, talking to the wolf that ate the village people. "You've been gone for too long." It was time for Cartoon to show what he had learned and what he was forecasting. "They got even war locked down now with drones and surveillance. But all we, the Homeys, got is war; all we know is war, violence, that splash and sizzle, but that shit doesn't even work anymore when they're hacking our brains, making our bodies useless. Who are we gonna fight when there aint even anymore land to take, which was all a big lie to begin with, that we can actually own anything, when the oil and minerals don't matter, but your attention matters, your brain attention—that's the new currency, but like always, it's all just

Monopoly Money

Buy on Boardwalk
Go bankrupt
Wander the streets
Homeless
Start another game or
Just steal more money from
The cardboard box and
You will play
All over again

It's Child's Play
That Lil villain
Chucky is the big winner
You may think you've won
But he owns the

Toy factory
Where they just
Print
More and more
Monopoly money

Toilet paper is
Actually
Worth more
But we value
Cesar
More than
God

The Pharisees
Tried to trick
Jesus
So they could kill him
Before his time
But he replied
'Give unto Cesar
What is Cesar's and
Give to God
What is God's'

He said
Fuck
Monopoly Money."

Cartoon knew the people of 2012 were addicted to brain-crack technology, that it was the biggest money maker in the history of humankind, so much so that even cash money was becoming meaningless. Dead Presidents were really dead. "Besides your brain matter, the only thing that's going to matter in the future is water, because that's all we really need. You can't even trust the food," Cartoon said schooling Lobo.

"The real danger," Cartoon continued, "Though, aint even the food, but the Clouds, poison clouds that rain down *basura*.

On the outside
(Which doesn't even fucking exist
Because it's all inside
An imaginary screen)
The social network
The invisible Cloud
Convinces you it's there to
Serve you
Help you connect
With others
Empower you

Underneath
(Which doesn't even fucking exist
Because it's all inside
An imaginary screen)
The social network is
Not
Pictures
Videos
Memes
Likes
Loves
It's actually
Algorithms
That are designed to
Help you
Confess
Not only to crimes but to
Nonsense

The algorithm's job isn't
To connect you but to
Keep your attention
So that it can study you
All of you
Your emotions
Your eyes

Your facial movements
Your intelligence
Your stupidity
Data stored in a
Nowhere Cloud
That rains
Who you are
Better than you can

Eventually
(If not already)
It knows you
Better
Than you know yourself

The point is not to sell you
Anything
The point is to
Steal your soul
For future consumption
Somewhere beyond
Capitalism
Because there is no
Capital
No 'things' are even necessary

The new economy is based on
Nothing
A monster of nothing
We are happy to hoard
Believing we are getting a
Great deal
Not understanding we are being
Eaten alive from
The inside out

More important
Than ever before:

Know yourself."

Cartoon kept a straight face.

"Man," Lobo responded turning up a satisfied and proud grin, "you seem to know what's actually happening." Lobo smiled, and the cracks in his face spread out wide. "It's like a Jungle sometimes, but I wonder

Is it history or
The future
That is the truth?" Lobo needed answers.

"Well, Lo," Cartoon replied ready, having trained for this moment for twenty years, "I know
I can't escape my past
I wake and see myself
All of the hauntings that
Don't wash off
That must be who I am,
But at the same time, during
A day and night's cycle

I dream away from myself
See surreal scenes of me and
Not me
Floating around in space
Laughing with dead people I never knew
Looking at myself and not knowing anything
That must be who I am."

Cartoon was trying to tell Lobo that it was both history and the future that was the truth and not the truth. Lobo nodded his head smiling, liked it, and not for posterity purposes, but he liked their conversation right there at that moment. But he also knew that even the moment was really not there.

"This present moment
Can't be reality
For it is fleeting."

Lobo, with his hands, grabbed at the air, the present moment, he could not hold, that escaped him, no matter how strong he was.

"Humiliating me
Always out of my grasp
That cannot be who I am."

Cartoon agreed with Lobo, did not have an answer, and that was ok for both of them.

"Somewhere in this madness
I exist
Somewhere in this insanity
I am the truth." Cartoon looked past the bullet proof glass, stared past Lobo at the white wall.

"Remember
Camarada
In this *selva*
Nadie se salva." Lobo knew this as the only answer.

"But I read and see what they're always trying to do, promising to do—save everyone. I even read they're trying to come up with some shit called a Universal Basic Income, give everyone their basic needs met, but aint no one gonna do that." Lobo rocked back on his steel stool. "It aint that we can't easily do it with all the bullshit monopoly money we steal and invent out of thin American air, but it's that outdated Puritan hard-work ethic myth that won't allow us to give people basic things like homes. Puritan, Pilgrim shit. Even though hard work is becoming useless cause computers will always work harder and more efficiently than us—even if we aint gotta work, we still believe that the devil will steal us to sin if we're just havin a good time! The upper classes aint gotta follow this rule, aint never followed this rule—cause it was always someone else doin all the hard work for nothin, especially the Blacks who built this country—but sure as fuck the rotten dumb asses gotta believe in hard work." In pity Lobo shook his head.

"They say I'm imprisoned, but it's them whose in cages. Shit, I'm better than them with their fancy meaning!

Meaning?

There is actually no such thing as
Efficiency

You Were Meant to Waste Your Life

Your life
Not any machines' mind
Which has no mind

But
The problem is that
You're taught only
Stupid people
Stop and smell
The roses
Because that is a
Waste of time

Smart people develop apps!

I thank God for my
Blessing to
Always have the
Will and Purpose of
Stupidity

Hallelujah!
I'm still able to
Embrace my own
Insanity."

Lobo was happy talking to Little Cartoon. Cartoon was happy listening to El Lobo. "So the bosses just aint gonna do it—give us peace and respite, a roof over our heads for free—instead they'll make up some bullshit work in order to enslave us to their ideals, to offer us some meaningless purpose of theirs while they pass it off to us as our own will. And the herd will thank them for allowing them to clean the corporations' toilets and having their brains filled with *kaka*, which is the new genius job: log in and tune out, out of yourself, out of your spirit. Sell your soul for nothing but invisible air. How many 'likes' will make me famous?" Lobo laughed a good hearted bottom-of-his-stomach laugh that echoed in the sealed windowless visiting room.

Cartoon chuckled from deep in his belly and slapped his own thigh, as if creating a new beat. "I'm absorbing all of this, Brother, and I'm getting it more and more, even as we speak: that's authentic education, communication."

Cartoon paused to think, wanted to make sure they were comprehending each other.

"Lobo?" he asked, "Tell me if this is right: It's that we can't get bogged down in their shit, cause that's their best weapon against us, misinformation—propaganda to make us take on their identity, but we gotta be gangsters, Homes. Understanding and undercover like a motherfucker.

You don't have to believe that words matter
Like you I know once a word is whispered
It is a lie
The word can never substitute for the thing
These letters are
Spider symbols
An inexact attempt at reality

Nevertheless,
I love a good lie
An entertainment
An engineering marvel
A web
Sticky and almost invisible
Waiting to capture its victim
The reader
The listener

These words were constructed with
Sweat and blood

Precision and grace
Patience
A plan
A horror story
Where you get tangled up
No escape
Except imagination
Your salvation
From the spiders
The spiders
The spiders

In your mind
You go beyond words
You make believe
Your own lies
Your own truth
The same thing

We all crawl and climb walls

They're gonna try to enslave us in new ways, Lobo, that's what I'm learning right now from you.

I get it
Freedom is supposed to be
Dynamic
The opposite of
Efficiency
Which technology
Educates us is
Everything."

Cartoon paused, shocked to hear his own words and ideas, the lessons he had learned and was only now, after twenty years, able to articulate. Then he resumed:

"First they're gonna make us

Stupid
Not smart
With this
Technology
Kaka
Then they're going to make us
Bored with
Reality

Then we are
Worse than
Dead."

Cartoon said it, and Lobo was satisfied with Cartoon's insights. Lobo held no guilt whatsoever for having kicked Cartoon out when he was only sixteen years old. His Odyssey had been fruitful.

"You learned some important shit on your journey, Cartoon." Lobo gripped the phone tightly, his knuckles ready to burst. "But the most important thing you learned was how to listen. You must have suffered a lot to know how to do that. Of course, I know that there are no shortcuts, no handouts.

Aint no one just gonna give you love
It don't work like that, baby
No one owes you a damn thing

So build them biceps
Brush your teeth in a circular motion
Most importantly—
Live your life like a fucked-up poem

Cause you can lie about everything else
But poetry is truth

You choose:
Pretend your shit don't stink
Or embrace the insanity of existence

By choosing the stink
You love life and life loves you
Take it any way you can get it."

    Lobo pounded his right fist against his heart.

    Could there be any better wisdom? Cartoon thought. "Bro, no matter how you must have suffered locked up all these years, you made game, got straight gamed up to the fullest, an example for us all."

    "Most people are all fucked up," Lobo warned, dismissing the compliment, "and thems the good ones! There's strength in numbers, but you first gotta be willing to go all the way *solo cholo*, like you've done for 20 years, but it aint like the old days, cause it's not about rushing the enemies with a shank. We need a Brain *Bushido*, a type of honor that involves thinking, warriorhood in your own brain in order to fight off the impurity of technology that wants to not even give us the opportunity to fight. It's not us who's obsolete; it's obedience that's obsolete. We don't even know what's going on, and I'm the one stuck here inside these prison walls! My mind is the product of this prison system, and in a way, it's been a blessing. All I got is my brain; they took everything else away. But you all out there got too many distractions and evil infecting you, taking you away from yourself." Lobo dropped his head in disappointment.

    In life there are sometimes moments of truth, irreversible instants that mean more than any moment.

    "From this day forward," Cartoon swore, understanding this life and death significance, "I vow my soul to getting our *gente* back to who we naturally are. We aint gotta necessarily go back to where we can never go back to, but we gotta know where we're from; we need the roots no one ever teaches us, that no technology cares about evolving in us. To delete the past, they're trying to convince us we're in a post-truth world, where anything can be invented and made true, but they use that language and those ideas to pacify and control us. We gotta keep truth in our hearts. We need to be amazed again, like we were in the beginning. WOKE. We need consciousness to be consciousness, whispers in the wind, which is who and what we naturally are." Cartoon had no time to waste or be unclear. He sit up straight, with focus. "Brother, we needed to critique first in order to create because without the critique we're just gonna keep ignorant and thinking everything is the way it's supposed to be. Problem is we don't learn the truth first; in school they feed us some shit we eat as the truth. But in order to really learn truth, we gotta learn lies, learn to smash the lies—then we can move from there." Cartoon considered his task. "I can be solo, will be, but we got other solid soldiers still out there, like Toro, like Santo's spirit, his son Lil Santo, even Maricela, especially mama Maricela. We'll figure some shit out.

Cause we are the roots. Us *locos* and *loca*s are all indigenous, of this earth. We are *familia* and tribes. That's the entire world, more so than any grand imagination of the concept of earth or even humanity. Brother Wolf, the abstraction of humanity does not do justice to the human being in front of me." Cartoon placed his palm against the bullet proof glass and touched Lobo's spirit. "You are with me now. You are with me, and I am with you. We together right now are the world. Family. Tribes."

Lobo was proud of and confident in Cartoon. Lobo placed his own palm against the glass, matching his hand against Cartoon's hand. Lobo thought Cartoon looked good, stylish, in command, lean and clean, with not a stray hair on his funny face. Lobo could not, however, send out a sheep amongst the wolves. He gave him *Neta*.

"Like me, you've chosen the route of suffering; it's an eccentric goal. You've chosen the torture of Mission Accomplishment, like crazy buffed Toro. That boy Lil Santo, he comes from good red blood, sick Santo and Mari. Hell yeah, she can share, too. You all can do some shit," Lobo squeaked with some fear in his voice, as he knew how hard it would be to do something you do not even know, especially when you do not know what you are doing!

"I need to pull your coat, give you something I hope can help when times get tough, something I've guarded and have never told anyone these past dozen years inside these walls, but it's been my mantra, my own personal code that gets me through the days and nights." Lobo did not want to share it, had kept these words guarded a dozen years.

"I'm here." Cartoon was listening. Lobo relaxed, tensed up, then exhaled:

"I hold honor, action courageously, live consciously, believe in faith, and prove love."

Cartoon did not say anything. He absorbed *amor*.

Lobo felt naked after he said it, but he was happy. He did not want to leave Cartoon with such heaviness, though, which Lobo knew could be a burden. He smiled his Lobo smile and told Cartoon to chill. "Take it from me, El Lobo, every once in a while, especially in the middle of the crazy shit

157

you are about to get into, you need to let yourself howl," Lobo pursed his lips and aimed his mouth to the ceiling. Cartoon looked up, and Lobo continued. "Howling soothes soul. It's better than any friend. The sound, the thunder, the homeboy who you always hoped for, giving you magic and mad love through the whirling of wind in the air that is your own music. It teaches you about you, who you really are and who you've forgotten. Can you remember the howl of your animal self? Not the crying of a baby, which we can never forget about ourselves, but the howling of the dog, the ape, the real homo sapien (wise man) inside yourself? That's the shit that helps more than any buddy or program or network of lost souls. Are you a friend to you, yourself? A friend to your forgotten voice?

Do you recognize yourself in the emptiness of the echo?

On Bernal Heights
Alone
I
El Lobo
Used to
Climb to the
Top of that mountain
To howl
I would strut to the edge of
The highest cliff
Wind swinging me wild
Pushing me forward
Pushing me off

To howl is a risk worth taking

On the streets
I always had to calm my urges
On the block
I had to stay silent
In my agony

But there
On Bernal Heights
I howled:

OOOOWWWWHHHH!

Is it a sin to sing soul?
To be proud of cries
To be transformed beyond
What little Red Riding Hood
And the three little pigs
Think of me?
Can't I just stand here
With my pain
And wretchedness
And beauty
And howl?

I don't want your food
I don't want your mind
I don't want your life
I ask for little things:

To howl
At sunshine and moon
To howl
At spirits
Before
With and
Beyond me
To let my tears fall
In peace
In love

Truth is
Confession and liberation
That
No one understands."

Lobo hung up the phone then finally stood proud, the way a wolf is
supposed to stand.

CHAPTER SEVEN — THE MISSION OF DOLORES

Me llamo La San Fran Misión de Dolores

Varrio of peace and pain

Born as a savior
San Francisco
Bald-in-the-middle monk
You taught me to find peace in blood

Dolores
Creek of sorrows
You cursed me the tears of a woman
True torture

I am floating in the ether
I am in every Homey's cup
In every junkie's needle
In every rat roaming around
The dirty *Misión*
Not the clean pristine paradise of
Native Ramaytush Ohlones

    I was not always *Misión Dolores*, the mother of pain. I was natural, jungle and woods, water and fire. I was the happy brown dirt that you cannot see covered now by sad gray cement. I was the original, that which has always existed. One day man pulled down the sun, and I became *Dolores*, the suffering of so much.
    Let me begin from before the beginning, which has no end.

The soul's goal is creation

If there is an alma
It is beyond us
But we find ourselves here
In this place

Now

So we try to remember and invent this
Blessing and curse
Inside
That we know is not us
But that we believe is after us

Ready to be born
Upon our death
Then will it live
But only when we are gone

The soul's goal is destruction

In this place were lava and darkness, lightning and thunder. It was
loco, the only way it knew to be, the natural sincere way of the universe.
Eventually the green grass grew. Colors of lavender, magenta, and turquoise
sprung everywhere. There was no name for such beauty. It had not been
corrupted by a lie such as beauty.

The people of the dirt, brown just like the ground, rooted in the mud,
natural, they came. They played. They made love. They lived and died and
appreciated the eternal spirit, which is all that there is.

Ashes to ashes
Dust to dust
Fantastic faith and
Utter imagination required:

Even the
Nothing
Even the
Suffering
Is a blessing

So, really, I have always been with them, the natural people, but my
name, the make-believe of suffering is new. It came with the pointy helmeted
people, the Spaniards. I was a simple creek running through the wilderness.

They saw me and loved me, for who does not love water? But they also predicted the pain that would fall from their steel swords. When they first witnessed my *arroyo* giving life to the future, they praised *la mas firme Nuestra Señora de Dolores*, Our Lady of Sorrows, the mother of God, Maria, who is usually depicted with seven swords piercing her sorrowful heart.

Forever I am mourning for Jesus Christ, my son. This pain has given me my identity.

Yes, it is an illusion

Whether or not it is true
Once we tell the story
It is truth more powerful than truth

Cristo came to this world through me
Born to serve stupid ungrateful humans
Who he knew would ultimately kill him
Yet still he volunteered to help and to save them
Mijo

I bore him for beggars and sinners and
For petty human beings
Who through him can believe in
Forgiveness and redemption and *amor*

Why would they murder my beautiful son?
When they named me *Dolores*, my water turned to blood.
But soon after they needed a new name to hide the truth of pain. On June 29, 1776, before the birth of the imagined United States of America, the holy priest officially named the Mission San Francisco de Asis. I am the most ancient structure still standing in the city. Saint Francis, the peaceful servant who could talk with animals, hid the truth beautifully. Using the lie of San Francisco, the pointy helmeted people enslaved and killed the Native Ohlones.

San Francisco may be a Saint and considered the champion of liberty, the capital of free love and flower power, but I tell you it is a lie. I challenge you to look deeply into yourself, into this place. My bloody tears, my painful life, at least, knows its own true story. But I understand

It is not for everyone:
Consciousness
With its
Intellectual acrobatics and
Overly elaborate interrogations of
Existence

Give most people some
Beer and barbeque
A roof over their heads
Some lies to read
Some laughs to catch
A clean, private restroom and
They are fairly fulfilled and
Happy

People don't need a cause or
Education or
Enlightenment or
Freedom
Stupid geniuses would rather be
Alive than
Free

Consciousness is stuff someone made up and
Damned us with
Because of the vanity of their words
The insecurity of their ego

No, no, no
We must not live for something or
Die for something
That is not true

We live and die simultaneously
We choose our own poison
We choose our own poetry

The poem and poison of San Francisco did not stay in the dreams of the Spaniards or, later, the Mexicans. The 18"49ers" eventually came to town, those dirty bearded lice-ridden diseased bums, and some others too, the Chinese, the Chileans, even some Africans. They came, but ultimately, by 1855, everyone was depreciated and dehumanized except for Whites. Whites Only deserved gold. With them came the new California dream, Manifest Destiny. No holy blessings from a Saint Francis needed. Kill what is natural and get rich quick.

Do you understand now that this great city of San Francisco is actually its own state?

A State of Emergency

Sirens
Sirens
Sirens

At some point the panic becomes passive
Then you understand
How even the devil can thrive in hell

Every day is an emergency
One day closer to the ultimate riot
Destruction
It lasts a long time
Yet it is really nothing at all
The blink of an eye
The scratch of an ass
Then it is over

A state is not an action
A state is prolonged perpetual torture

Bullshit

You can smile in between the yanking of your fingernails
Everything begins and
Everything ends

Just like the sea
Just like the stars
Just like that time you were crying alone twisted in bed and the whole world
was armed against you because you deserved damnation
Just like the fires that burned in Baltimore and Watts and Guatemala
The mysterious fires that are burning down houses and kicking out the people
of the Mission
The fires in your barbeque pit

What matters is the
Action
Not the state of being
You can down a beer while the *carne asada* cooks
You can raise your fist as you drown
You can pick up a pen and write
Because we all know the story of the pen:
Once upon a time a simple man pulled out his pen against the swords and
guns aimed at his heart
And
With full faith he shouted:

"The pen is mightier than the sword!"

They mowed him down instantly

That is why I, the Spirit, am telling you this story, so that it is written, so
that you can understand the emergency.

The Mission, *La Misión*, my *Dolores*, grew to become the most
powerful city on planet Earth. Saint Francis preached the dream, not of
peace, but of power and greed, lust and liberty. It created millions of converts
rushing to glittering gold mountain. In the late 1800's, *La Misión* was the
stomping ground for bear and bull fights. The lands around my nearly
abandoned mission church became a place of death, one for gambling and
dueling—for settling your business like a stupid man.

By 1906 when the great quake destroyed the rest of the city, I, *La
Misión*, was the only structure that stood strong. When downtown crumbled,
I became a headquarters, and more people began to discover my beauty. By
the 30's the Italians, the Irish, the Polish, they spread all over 18th Street,

Folsom, Capp Street, and my own namesake, Mission. It was a bustling time. People began to confuse the Mission, the goal, the reality that was happening, and perhaps, they, too, predicted the future: the locals, instead of calling me *Misión* San Francisco de Asis, they called me, *Dolores*, Mission Dolores, the name of the Catholic parish, the name of the fancy basilica. Am I beauty or am I pain? Am I mud hut or colorful stained glass? This confusion is the root of who I am.

During the 1940-1960's, lots of *Californios, Mexicanos, Nicoyas, Chapines, Salvatruchos, y más* immigrated to my earth. Some of them had been kicked out from their original *varrio* on Rincon Hill. The city officials said they had to hand over their homes for progress, the creation of the western landing of the Bay Bridge. Once the Homeys came, the white people started leaving, but, unlike the myths that exist, it was never white flight. It was that the whites had promise for something else, the post-World War II American Dream. The government gave them the sweetest candy, fully subsidized white-picket-fenced homes in segregated places like Walnut Creek, Danville, Alamo. The Mission Latinos were forbidden to purchase homes in the whites only world, so they were stuck and also blessed to build community, the *varrio*.

I like these people. Brown like the dirt, they love truth, just like the Native Ohlones had. Different shades of brown, they dance and party in their poverty. They laugh through their deaths—*Dia de Los Muertos*. And I even laugh at myself for being so sad, full of *Dolores*, which is unnatural. They have so much to be sad about, but they carry class,

Grace:
The free and unmerited favor of God
As manifested in
The salvation of sinners and
The bestowal of blessings

I deliver to you
News
Not solutions
But
Torments people go through
Trying to solve problems
Clashing voices

Morbid moral tortures

Their struggles are
What help us with our own
Suffering
No sensationalism
Just gutter truth
Humanism

Some sin
In order to
Enjoy confession
Others do it as an
Exorcism
With a heavy heart
Full of shame and disgrace
Routes, too, to reality

This state of
Confusion and brutality are
Blessings
You know you are
Alive
Full of anxiety
Awake at 3:00 in the morning
Mumbling Hail Marys and
Our Fathers
Knowing they cannot
Help you

Troubled inside
You find
You own your mistakes
Like in chess
When you move the queen
To her death
It cannot be taken back

It is independence
No one understands you
You are beyond understanding or
Pity
Alone
Isolated
Outcast
With the world everywhere around you
Yet you are not in it

It is a state of grace
To figure out
How to get out of
Or
More into
Your own
Shit

   La gente did both, figured out reality better than any school textbooks
and also got more into the depth of their own diarrhea, angel dusted on the
streets, lost in space, outer space, beyond my territory, shouting to the stars
and screaming at illusions, singing in the middle of the night on Army Street,
taking vacations to the mental ward on the 7th floor of General Hospital or to
the county jail at 850 Bryant Street, the Hall of Justice, the House of Horrors.
   The 1990's brought the beginnings of gentrification. First they tore
down the Army Street Projects, kicked out Black people, then lawfully
passed gang injunctions: rounded up all the Homeys and demonized them,
had even their own family and community members asking for the Homeys'
annihilation, without knowing that they were simply volunteering for their
own demise, because the big boys at City Hall would push them out next.
Mass incarceration, desperation, drug addiction, and also pride in this
place—for when you have nothing else, at least you have the air you breathe,
the air you pretend to own.

Many
Gente have died
Killed
For my streets

Tattooed my
Misión
All over
Their arms
Chests
Necks
Hearts
Beautiful calligraphy and
Olde English
Cholo script

The *cholos* y *cholas*
Always made my
Dolores
Feel
Lovely

In the new millennia, the 2000's, the mass deportations, a.k.a. gentrification, of Native gente erupted out of the Mission. All of a sudden, these houses that served the poor, that a pobre could purchase back in 1977 for twenty or thirty thousand dollars, became worth more than one million dollars! It was the same exact house, at the same exact spot; the door knobs were not transformed into gold, yet out of pure evil, the developers and speculators were now forcing segregation all over again. Just like the signs of the past:

Whites Only

A 1.6 million dollar sign in front of a home on York Street is the new "Whites Only" sign. Whites only can afford these homes. It was the returning cycle of the people of the dirt to be

Kicked Out

The Homeboy tattoo true:
Smile Now, Cry Later :) :(

It was a boast and compliment to be kicked out—
Of school
Of church

Of civilization
Only the streets were where savages belonged

Even donut-holed cops knew the Homeys owned
Las calles
So that was their goal:
To be joined with streets
Concrete at their feet
Beers mixed with tears
Angeldust til they bust
Laughing at infinity: *Por Vida*

With pride and panic
They learned
Even infinity has its limits
Because they had to pay

My treasured gray cement and
Beautiful black tar
No longer loves them

I
Dolores
Break their hearts

Now is later

A new evil emerged by the 2010's. Disruptive destructive technology stormed into town. It did not want grace. It wanted its own self-justification. It did not want the patience of the natural world. Instead, it demanded to take credit for its own righteousness. It preached that gentrification makes everything better. Less crime, for example. But the desperate people who were kicked out did not simply vanish off the face of the earth. They, with their oppression, simply moved to other lands, sisters called Pittsburgh, Antioch, Stockton, Modesto, burgeoning rural slums. The new San Francisco 49ers hipsters with their big beards never really cared about saving anyone from crime and injustice. They cared about new gold, their own ways, thought they knew better than the Natives what to do with the land because technology loved micro-Bro-weries better than barbeque joints, cafes with laptop plugins better than barbershops, boutique stores selling fifty dollar t-shirts better than 99 cent discount stores. Gray and black houses were better than pretty colors of green, blue, yellow, and red. They were literally erasing the natural colors of the universe and pretending it was evolution, but it was not; it was just a poor imagination based on the unnatural lie of money and wealth, which they mistook for as power. The new crowd believed in progress more than humanity, and this made it easier for the Natives to be likened to animals.

The Mission became a hunting ground, and the brown people of the dirt were the ones being hunted, hunted by educators that failed them, politicians that poisoned them, police that killed them. Mysterious fires were burning down buildings and blocks, chasing out the poor people from the Mission. The empty lots then became prime opportunity for the building of luxury condominiums that would house no one except the wealthy. The *cholos* y *cholas* remaining responded with their art and culture, with their lowriders bouncing: Our Mission, NO Eviction. They had nowhere else to go except to go back to who they always were and always will be. The *locos* y *loca*s transformed it from Smile Now to Fight Now, sang only to

Fight Now!

Orita

The answer to everything is
Now
Yesterday is gone forever
Tomorrow is impossible
There is only
One answer to
Everything:

Orita

The comfort of nostalgia and/or
The imagination of a future
Is not

Now

If you understand or
Feel

Orita

There would be
No more
To learn
No more
To accomplish

Now
Makes
Our lives
Complete

They are still here bouncing, fighting! They are living life, these cartoon characters: Cartoon, Toro, Santo the Spirit, Alex Neta, Lil Santo, Maricela, *y más*! They are doing something to tap the source, not to pretend a solution, but to be part of the eternal struggle, which is nature itself. They hear me in the wind and feel me through the dirt. They know I am rooting for them, for they are the roots. *La gente* are fulfilling their roles in this tragedy, and these *pinches cholos* y *cholas*, they are making *Neta*, natural *Neta*, the way it truly is, which is not a tragedy or a comedy, but simply drama.

It is good literature
If the main characters
Understand
How stupid
They are

It does not need a plucking
Out
Of eyes
Or
A tragic

To be or not to be
Speech

Great stories
Simply
Go on

Time
Oblivion
Crushes us all
It is not special magic

So tell your story
The way it is
Admit your
Idiocy
Your
Humanity
And you are
On your way to
Greatness
Empathy
Honesty
Ultimately
Nothing
That which we all share

One day
One night
The seats will be empty and
The curtain will simply
Fall

CHAPTER EIGHT — THE GRAND CAPITALIST

In the spring of 2013, there was a story circulating on the San Francisco streets that He had resurrected, returned, and was gifting love (the miracle), to human beings, those down and out wretched folks in the dumps. He shook hands and embraced all. He gave away the bread of life. And it was for this, He was marked as the worst, most dangerous criminal in the entire system. On Sixth and Mission, under cover of darkness, the SWAT team charged, guns ablazing, and arrested the Son of Man who looked like a simple hobo. After interrogating Him and gaining no response except for empty eyes, they brought Him to a special judge at 850 Bryant, The Hall of Justice, The House of Horrors.

With glory and pomp, The Grand Capitalist, guided in by two senior sheriffs, strutted into the jail's psychiatric ward pod. Dressed in a sharp red single-breasted sharkskin suit, crisp white shirt, red silk tie, and spit-polished black oxford wingtip shoes, Grand wore white felt gloves that protected his precious soft hands that were used to command. Grand's face was a strange orange hue that no one dared call strange.

Grand took a seat across from Him who was wearing nothing except for an adult sized diaper—because He had been constrained to suicide watch and was not even allowed toilet privileges. He was a Brown man with hair like wool, unshaven, unkempt, a homeless creature, the most despised swine in their system.

"I know who you are. Figured you'd have come a long time ago to save your sheep, but no, you did not answer their prayers. There was only me, their true savior." Grand smiled shiny white diamond teeth. "You have no one to blame except for yourself." Grand waved over Him. "And now, look at you." Grand's face dropped in disappointment.

Sitting silent, lips closed, heart open, He, with a funky stink and hollowed out black eyes, looked into Grand.

"So, you been out starting shit, *ay*? For what? You actually think I don't have enough food or homes to give them? You think you are the only one capable of those miracles? Don't you know that all I got to do is snap my fingers and every single person on planet earth is fed, housed, and fulfilled? I, not you, have the power right now to make everyone a millionaire! And it will in no way bankrupt me because I simply invent the number, and it is reality!" Grand beat his breast as if it were a giant drum.

"What can you do sitting there all stupid?"

He sat silent and paid attention, while the Grand Capitalist was happy, proud that even the King of Kings must submit.

"What to do with you? My special enemy of the state." Grand stood up, the creases on his red pants still sharp. He sauntered in a circle, and in his mind he quietly entertained medieval torture, considered holding a good old-fashioned barbeque burning at the stake. "No, I do not need torture. I do not need to feed you to the lions or feed you to the flames, especially so that you can become some kind of martyr. Here in my era, in this twenty first century, I am beyond needing torture, because I am more human than you could ever have imagined— compassionate, giving, intelligent." Grand was giddy, mouth opened wide. "My punishment is humane and merciful. For the rest of your life, eternity, I will imprison you in a crystal palace where you will play games, chess and kites, *wilas*. Pelican Bay State Prison, Homes! Tomorrow I will ship you to the SHU—Security Housing Unit, lockdown 23 hours a day. Lots of naps. No escape." Grand jigged and was pleased with his solution, delighted in his genius. The two armed sheriffs shuffled their feet inside their shoes.

"Am I cruel?" Grand confronted Him. "This is necessary, utilitarian. I am the good guy. Allow me to explain:

You fucked up, confused them with hope. Now you have no right to add or change anything to what you said before, because once you open your mouth with your stupid wisdom, you actually curse them all to hell. Humans are too stupid to know what is good for them, such fickle creatures." Grand thought he almost saw Him smile.

The Grand Capitalist snapped:

"Do not think they actually love you. They love you today, but will help me send you to your doom tomorrow, for that is what I will tell them to do. They believe in and know me. They will forget You when You are at the Supermax Pelican Bay Prison. They will make excuses that they do not even have money for stamps!" Grand loved his own jokes. The sheriffs laughed.

"You fucked up when you gave them freedom, for freedom of faith is a torture, a horrible wicked punishment. Rebels can never be happy. They suffer. They drop out of school. They think they have the answers to nothing and then get frustrated with themselves, finding no peace in freedom." Grand was serious.

He did not move in his chair. He kept his hands on his naked knees.

"It is Your fault." Grand pointed down at him. "You gave us the right, first by giving love to lepers on the streets, then others organized the church, which led to total bloodshed, millions murdered, and a perversion of any holy message You had. That then morphed into a racket, the greatest system ever created, and not by God, but by the genius of human beings—Capitalism." Grand stood straight, took off his white gloves, showcased his bony white hands and gold-ringed fingers.

"You, you, what the fuck did you do but give them contradictory images that they can never understand, for you speak of a world, a heaven, they can never see, and what the fuck does that mean to men and women that need to see?" Grand's eyes pushed far out of his face.

He, sitting like a student, kept his eyes sunk into his soul.

"Humans can't make sense of freedom. Humans understand and love bread, real bread. You should have chosen to give them perpetual bread instead of some crazy impossible idea about perpetual life. And since you couldn't do it, now it is I who have created perpetual bread with my genetic modifications, GMO's—towering tomatoes, outrageous oranges, super cows! My science destroys your stupid temple with all of its mysticisms and superstitions. Nature bows before me."

The Grand Capitalist's red contrasted starkly against the dull gray room.

"Humans are like ants, too insignificant to be free. Obedience—they love it. Freedom has become unbearable and fearful to them. You more than anyone should know the sickness of humans. Agonizing freedom leaves them in hell. This is Your fault, Your Father, Your Son; it is bad family, bad parenting to give them freedom they cannot handle. It cannot be love to let your children suffer so much. You must hate them." The Capitalist, his face turning even more of a burnt orange, clenched his fists and looked at Him with fury, ready to punch him, to bully the weak-looking hungry Son of Man.

He simply sat there hearing sharkskin's gruffy voice.

"They love authority, miracles, not mystery! People can't reject a miracle, but instead of giving them what they want and need, you leave them alone, abandoned, at three o'clock in the morning, trying to believe in something they cannot ever see or hear or understand. When they need you most, you are not there." The Grand Capitalist was spitting his best logic.

"Man seeks miracles, and if you do not give them to him, he creates them. That is what I have done. I am a good man. I multiplied more powerfully than multiplying loaves of bread during a stupid sermon on the mount. I created new mounts—property. I created technology, the ultimate icon."

Sitting on the cold steel chair, He closed his eyes and took a deep breath in.

"But, no, you refused to enslave them with your miracles. I, on the other hand, am not too humble to showcase my magic, and that is why they love me more than they love you." Grand towered over Him.

"You expected them to be at your level? How many? How many in all these centuries, these millennia, have been at your level, ready to be burned in your name, how many did you simply leave in torture? How many lives did you waste?" Grand imagined Him suffering, listening and regretting.

He did not look away. He just sat there, ears open intently.

"Once they figure out your lies, have wasted their lives, they curse your name, but it does them no good. Their blasphemy makes them even more unhappy and confused! That is what your love and free will gives them—unhappiness, confusion, torture."

The uniformed sheriff guards put their hands on their holsters.

"I, we, give them something new and powerful, a mystery they can truly believe in, for they do not know exactly how my system works, but they trust it nonetheless because they feel its real effects on their lives. We, the human geniuses, relieve them from their existential crisis and guilt. The logical, intelligent mystery is what they must obey, not their own stupid conscience, which gives them no answer. We lift their torments from them with things, gadgets, Capital!"

"And now in *Anno Domini* 2013, because of the science of technology, the new capital is not even a thing, but nothing, just like You are nothing! I have mastered You more than you have mastered even Yourself! Everything I give them is in a make-believe illusory Cloud. They obey the Cloud that they cannot see, and believe in and connect it to our thing called money that they believe actually has value simply because I command that it has value. And they do not betray me!"

Grand was in a groove, in a frenzy, and did not want or need to say it, but he said it anyway, out of spite: "I don't want Your love because I don't love You."

Absorbing everything, He sat still following with His gaze the Capitalist walking and bouncing around.

"We are not with you; we are with it: Technology. Perfection. Two plus two! Who can deny that? We use technology for our advantage to gain this kingdom on Earth. Ultimately the beast of Technology will wash our feet with its blood. We are the Gods, not it.

"We control it." Grand was smug and sure of smart humans' power, could not imagine they were in any way enslaved by their own scientific

Frankenstein monster.

"We show stupid humans that they can only be free if they give up freedom and submit to our intelligence, the computers' algorithms. Then the herd just lives without worrying about freedom. Eventually they stagger quietly to meet their deaths. That is the best solution we can give them, and it is working. We do not need you."

His naked scrawny chest heaved up and down, His back pressed against the cold steel chair.

"I am not afraid of you and your impotent power. I was stupid once, but I made the courageous choice to serve madness no longer." An overwhelming feeling of hatred overcame Grand, and though he prided himself as being a logical player, Grand knew emotion was taking over.

"If anyone ever deserved our prisons, it is You." The Grand Capitalist commanded it with spite, with a seething revulsion that dripped from his lips. Grand said it intentionally to hurt Him, to kill Him.

The Son of Man knew it, understood, and accepted the brutal truth: The Grand Capitalist had made an excellent irrefutable human argument using solid genius logic.

But it is not Love, which is beyond logic.

With pure spirit, He rose to his feet, stepped forward in a precise motion, and planted a Judas Jesus kiss on the Grand Capitalist's cracked lips. The sheriff guards tackled Him to the floor.

He did not fight back.

CHAPTER NINE — LIL SANTO

It is February 14, Valentine's Day 2014. I am the product of true love, the union between *La Loca* Maricela and Sick Santo. It's my birthday. I just turned 22.

Today
I live the
Day of being
Older than
My father Santo was
When he died

For twenty two years
I've waited for this day
To see if I would
Explode

How can it be that right now
In my body
At this point in time
My father had already stopped breathing?
How can it be that as of today
I am wiser than my own father?

Today I am
An old man

From now on
He
The legend
Would have to come
To me
For advice
And what would I tell him?

Nothing
No one

Can help you with the
Truth
Except you

Not this poem
Not an old man
Not even destiny

No
No one
Only you
Look into your own
Abyss

Anyone who says they
Know
Doesn't know
Shit

It is your
Choice
How to live your
Life
It is your
Choice

I wander down
The block
Sit down
On a barstool
Shoot
Straight
Tequila

Fire tastes good

That is old man
Wisdom

Back in 2006 when I was a youngster of fourteen, I began tattooing. I'd been drawing my whole life but wanted to get to the next level. I wanted a special piece of art for my first, and even though my generation didn't get down anymore with the radiant *Pachuco* cross, I wanted it for the father, the legend, I never knew. With Indian ink smothered on a threaded needle, I quickly tapped it into my left hand, in between my index finger and thumb, that blank space of human canvas destined for the

Tattooed Cross

The light is your shadow
I cannot look directly at you
Because
You blind me

Flame
Burning bush
Overwhelming awe

You cannot shelter me
Nor
Can I shelter you
That is what it is

Being in love with
That which is
Beyond light

I will never know you

The myths about you are lies
They try to explain
That which is unexplainable
From a time
When we had few tools to do it
Language was new
What else could we do but
Make believe?

Nevertheless
They were pure stories
Those shamanic scriptures
That helped us and
Damned us
More than our
Grunts

Maybe
Theology
Technology
A blade of grass
A lotus flower
Is our answer
Most likely
We will never know
But it is there
Something
Beyond light

I make a fist
Feel my might
You are always
With me

Am I talking to God or my Santo *Cholo*? Is he talking to me, through me? My dear dad, the one they tell me walked the main line alone, who always sacrificed himself for Homeys, lived and died like that. *Barrio Bushido*. Shit, OG's still stop me on the streets, expect something else out of me, but I'm just who I am. I got his name, but I'm not especially holy, just a regular street kid, an aspiring artist who uses his art as a weapon for our empowerment.

My mama is *La Loca* Maricela, the homegirl who had me while she was caged in a zoo. Love that woman. I know she was hard on me growing up, just by being who she is, a *loca*, a convict, a cleaner, and lots more. I feel them both, and no matter what they were or are, they are the best, *amor*, all I could ever hope for in this fucked up world. I am rooted from hugs and kisses! I didn't have much when I was growing up, but that made shit even more fun, like when I used to steal and sell our

Foodies

Under the mattress
Stuffed way underneath
Was mama's favorite
Hiding place for
Green dollars and
Purple orange red
Government issued
Food stamps

Mama Mari didn't have any spare change so
She laughed at an allowance for me
It was my fault I was
Too little
Too lazy
To have a real job
She made me go to school
Where I would become smart and saved
But I was a stupid kid and wanted
Potato chips, Ho-Hos, sunflower seeds, and sodas more than
Books and tests and any teacher's wisdom
I wanted the
Strength of the streets

Sometimes the only thing she had hidden
Were food stamps
They were prettier than the other money but also
More of a hassle
More of an adventure
So I would steal the packet of red purple blue bills
Looking like cotton candy and
I learned to hustle down at
The corner liquor store on Shotwell Street and sell them to
Little old ladies who loved a great bargain
Twenty for ten

They never asked any questions
Were grateful for
Smiled at
The little boy with spunk

I became older and school had not saved me
I still stole but instead of buying
Twinkies
I sold the
Foodies and
Bought beers
Beers for all the Homeys!
We would laugh and live and love!
Our party paid for by
The United States of America's
Monopoly money
Money meant to humiliate us
Humiliate Mama
In their wicked game

These many years later
I do not regret my sin
It was better that
I stole than
Learned lies

Two years ago, back in 2012, this cat Cartoon ran up on moms and reminded her that he had known my dad real well, was his crime partner, said he had been gone for twenty years, that he wanted and needed to meet me, Santo's son, and talk with me, share something.

We went for it.

He was a funny looking kinda tall lanky dude, old school, maybe 36 or 37 years old. I could tell he was from here, but he had a crazy look, like a thousand yard stare full of trauma and urgency. We met at Taco Loco on 29th Street, where he said he and my pops used to kick it sometimes. He bought me a Mexican Coca Cola, and we sat at a booth next to the big window overlooking Mission Street. We waited for our carne asada super burritos.

"*TODO BODO* DOWN," His words startled me. Was nigga trying to flex? I didn't know, but he kept talking.

"Lil Santo." Cartoon pierced into my eyes, my green grenades given to me by my father who died before I was born. "One night back in the days, your pops, your jefe, Santo, Rest in Peace—damn, you're handsome just like him—came to my pad snapped out—angel dusted, yet understanding. Standing stoned straight, he paused in my little living room and with dignity and a new knowledge from somewhere in the beyond, he snorted the following words:

'*Todo Bodo* Down. I'm *Todo Bodo* Down, *ese!*'"

Cartoon said it to me like if I should understand what the fuck he was talking.

"What is that, blood?" I asked with clenched fists.

"Lil Santo, your papa knew some things. With authority, with a sneer, with certainty about identity, he proclaimed the answer for the entire *varrio.*" Cartoon calmed me down. He wasn't talking shit; he meant what he was saying as a compliment to my dad. I unknotted my fists.

"Those words meant nonsense," Cartoon continued, "but they also meant it all—everything in one nut phrase. A phrase he invented and that only the few chosen Homeys knew and understood." He chuckled. "Sometimes we would joke about it: homeboys would rib Santo and greet him with '*Todo Bodo* Down!' We would drink up, smile, and shout to the stars. Then sometimes, after being confused for so long and being bitter and afraid and angry and straight *loco*, the homeboys would take the smirks off of their faces, and they would almost cry it out. That was '*Todo Bodo* Down' with a seriousness, with a desire for forgetting. And when it was time to fight or do something completely insane, we would chant it '*Todo Bodo* Down. *Todo Bodo* Down.' Then it was a prayer. They were magical words that woke the spirits we needed to help us. *Todo Bodo* Down contained the natural purpose for our entire existence."

"You're making a joke, right, cause you're a Cartoon?" I didn't get his humor. These were different times. "I don't get how that is the answer to anything, man."

Cartoon took a deep breath. He knew what I needed to know. He explained: "*Todo* is all. *Bodo* is a corruption of nothing and everything; it is a word that sounds good and rhymes with *Todo*. *Bodo* can mean fucked. It can mean total. It can mean whatever you want it to mean as long as you place the spirit in there with it. Down doesn't mean out. Down in this context means up. Down means committed. Down means sure/certain. Down means knowing. And what is it that we know?" He was asking me, so I told him.

"I don't know; I don't get it," I answered.

"You got your father's blood in you." Cartoon grinned. "I don't know; we don't know, yet the answer is still there. It cannot be articulated any better." He reached his right hand out for the homeboy handshake, *carnal* style, with the palm up, not to the side for square bears. I slapped my palm into his.

"*Todo Bodo* Down. All fucked up. All into life. All ready for the next step. All hurt yet still standing," Cartoon said it sincerely.

"All is *firme*," I responded. We gripped hard. I was being initiated into the old school *cholo* world. Maybe this is what I was always destined to do, I thought. My Santo *Cholo* floated throughout the air.

A sexy *señorita* delivered our super spicy burritos, and we chowed em down. Taco Loco got the good greasy ones.

Afterwards I asked him, "So now what?"

"Movement," he said. "I been to see Lobo, who is like your uncle, who's serving life in Q, and we are carrying on your father's spirit. That's what we need: Movement."

"You talkin about revolution or what?" I had been hearing that shit my whole life livin in the Mish.

"I'm talking about Movement, our natural state of being, like a river running, never static, always progressing. Movement of education. Movement of art. Movement of power. *La Movida* of insanity, *Vida Loca*, Homes," he said it with a snarky *cholo* accent.

My Homey Alex Neta walked into the joint, wearing his bouncer uniform, black boots and all. He must have had to go to work later at Tip Top's nightclub on San Bruno Avenue. He said what's up, and I told him to sit down and peep some game. Cartoon mad dogged Alex, as if he weren't part of the crew, maybe even thought Alex was some sort of cop. "This nigga is solid, Cartoon," I said.

"Then if he's solid," Cartoon kept staring down Alex, and Alex did not look away, "What's up with the Movement, Homes?!" Cartoon asked it and opened his palm out to Alex for the homeboy handshake. Alex smiled his Alex Neta smile. He didn't know how to answer, but he gripped Cartoon's hand and mad dogged him lovingly. We laughed. Cartoon looked happy. We were youngsters compared to him. He started telling stories about where we were.

"Young bloods, do you know you are in the seed of it:

The city of Inten
Intensity
In
Ten
City
San Fran
Vida Loca

The seed of it
Roots
Rising
Roots that never got the chance to bloom
Sunk into dirt
Underneath the Earth
Roots
Veins

'Too much
He's
Too much'
My mother would say it
With a
Smile
And a
Broken heart
Her varicose veins
About to burst

Bernal Heights,"

Cartoon pointed up to his left side out the big window, "is

Rocky ground
High hill
Homeboys
Would carve into
Desks in
Juvenile Hall

'Cortland Hill
Where
The pimpin is real'

La Misión
The seed is
Down in the valley
Santo, your pops,
Held the line on
21st and Folsom
Chasing cars and
Dreams
He refused to believe
Were
Nightmares
No
It was just another story
Another
Poem
He had to pay for
In the future

I get butterflies
Thinking about
The seeds I have
Planted
The weeds I have
Worn
The life
I have lived
It has been life
Amor
It has been lots of
Love

I got nothing to regret."

Cartoon looked at peace, and that is something spectacular in this warzone. Alex and me looked at each other, nodding our heads, knowing this nigga was crazy, and exactly what the fuck we needed in order to build some type of *Movida*.

That was it, our first function.

From then on, from 2012 to right now in 2014, when I'd see Alex, who is like five years older than me, I'd be like, "What's up with the Movement, Homes?!" And I'd say it with a snarky ass *cholo* accent just like Cartoon's. Me and Alex would test each other. Locking onto my eyes, he would uplift his sly smile, and we would embrace in the homeboy hug, all love, the love of lost souls brought together by the streets and stupidity, marks of men from the city.

"*Ah huevo*, Homes!" Alex would hammer it home to the Homes, me, Lil Santo, and with his response I always knew it was on. What's up with the Movement?! Your nutsack, nigga! Get it all and let it out: extract your essence. At first the Movement must've been about drinking bottle after bottle of beer, downing stiff straight shots of cheap tequila, smoking them crazy skunky blunts, singing songs, and lowriding in Alex's pristine red Monte Carlo, the one they used as a model for that Balmy Alley mural, rolling through las *calles*, the hood, the tourists' spots, Twin Peaks, crooked ass Lombard Street, the Wharf—the entire city was ours, and they knew it, all them city dwellers watching us ballet down the block in such strange vanity. It was our city, our history, our tar and cement that had never stopped loving us, even though many of us had gotten kicked out and lived in other jungles across the Bay. Alex and I had each other and that's all we needed for any Movement, cause we moved, cruised, struck out to the windy beach for no reason except to go, and if we needed the beach to crash upon her just like the waves do to the shore, then she was there for us—like my mama Maricela had always been there for me, like *La San Fran Misión* was always there for us.

I remember one time in 2013, we took a twelver to the Cliff House cave, and we kicked it on rocks, and the waves, yeah, they crashed, and the day was nice, not too cool, not too hot, that San Francisco April weather that you get if you're lucky, once all the fog burns away. We didn't say shit. Had the oldies and *corridos* playing, and I must have rewound "Never, Never Leave Me" by Mary Wells, our honorary African-American chola, like 50 times, and with all the shit I was into at that moment in my life, juggling around *la Vida Loca*, I let loose, like a howling wolf, and I knew my Brother Alex, he wouldn't mind the transformation. Cause for everyone else I couldn't let that shit show, but for him, I could be vulnerable, and the motherfucker wouldn't hold it against me. Alex Neta didn't try to counsel me or save me or comfort me. He let me cry it all out and be real, the only way we knew how, with some *cervezas* and Chicano power, *Cholo* identity created on these American streets and that we utilized to live life like stars in the sky, cause the *Indios* know astronomy better than any of them suits and boots marching through downtown, in the courthouse, under the schoolhouse, or at the police station.

Alex loves the legends, has respect and wants their authentic education and spirit. He can't get enough of the street stories of my father, El Santo, who gave it all up for all the Homeys. In me, Alex must feel the impossible love that my pops Santo and mama Maricela made out of all this insanity. I give Alex all that love from the *varrio*, and that's what pushes us forward to do what we do for perfect strangers, our brothers and sisters.

Every once in a while we check in with Crazy Cartoon, that OG that got good game and that set us on this journey with no clear destination. He's doing some outer space shit, his own thing, connecting with organizations, writing, speaking, starting shit. At Taco Loco, our headquarters, Cartoon sits us down and schools us. One time he brought over Toro, that bull that starts all that bullshit on 25th and Capp, who fights at the drop of a dime. They just started rapping right there, like if we weren't even around, and we knew it was a privilege to listen and learn.

"You got these *locos* on a mission, huh?" Toro checked us. "You know how we used to do it?" He scanned us, the smoke rising from his nostrils.

"14 years oldie snapped out
In alleys and emergency rooms
Such stupidity despair and
Amor

I would be napping in the creaks of narrow driveways
Behind the McDonald's pissed-on alleyway off 24th Street
Waking in the womb
Of the *varrio*
Then I'd hike the hill to the top of
Bernal Heights Mountain
Singing laughing fucked up
Knowing
Everything was fine

I was just an average guy dropout dumb fuck wetback warrior angel dust
head from the San Fran Mishon *matons* K.J. Killer Joints
It was a dying business and breed of *cholo* that was still sucking in foul
rubber tire scents and that's how you knew it was the good shit

An average guy

Who could use the dust dreams for daring and progress and average-ness
Like getting killed or going to *la pinta* or flying off a cliff of this giant
mountain called war in San Quentin or Kuwait or
The restroom
International motherfucker cause wherever you go you are there and
It's time to fight and learn even if that means
Death
Which is the best education ever learned beyond any academic institution or
insane asylum."

Toro snorted and smiled at us.

After hearing this kind of inspiration, me and Alex would go and
shoot for more movement. We would invent shit together, take risks, not
gangmember type risks of the 1980's and 90's, but new natural, more
dangerous risks, emotional risks. Cause we knew by doing *movida*, we'd
be challenging everything we'd ever learned about manhood, intelligence,
effectiveness, and *amor*—cause we were going far outside any system, back
to roots.

Alex would have all these crazy ideas: "Let's do poetry out on the street.
Get together a band, some homegirls, and spit out some words on the streets.
Fuck that, let's do poetry right next to the *loco* murals on Balmy Alley, the
ones you help paint, Lil Santo!" So we did that shit and had a blast, got
people together and developed community. "Let's get a Carnaval booth this
year in 2013. We'll get a pullup and dip bar so Homeys on the street can hit
pullups and dips as we do our thing, sell t-shirts, pour water for the thirsty,
and pick up on some ladies, too!" We were calling out all the out-of-shape
homeboys and fine homegirls and the little kids and making them hit up their
weight. We took photos with hella cheeses, everyone loving what we stood
for. "Let's lowride cruise in my Monte Carlo everywhere and give love to
the *gente* on the streets!" We'd pull over at the bus stops on Mission, down
Folsom, on Bryant, and kidnap grandmas and mamas with their midgets and

groceries and take them in style to their destinations, laughing and singing all along the way.

We didn't just talk about *Movida*; we actually did it, made things happen, made things move! And each time we did something loving and beneficial for the people we got even braver and bolder and would laugh and talk about new things to do to spread loving *locura*, our natural state, the way we were always intended to be. After our struggles on the streets and in society, we knew there was no hope in the system. Too much corruption and cowardice. The best way to transform the world was the way we were doing it—with love and action on the actual streets, a little bit at a time.

Alex is older than me, so maybe he has to make shit complicated sometimes. This past New Years, 2014, we were kicking it together with our ladies, celebrating new possibilities, but something else was tugging at him. He knew something, felt something.

"I've been thinking about what we've been doing for the past two years, been wanting to let go of some ideas. New Years is a good time to let shit go," Alex said.

"Go for it, Bro," I said. Our ladies were listening, too. I had a cute honey from the City College schoolhouse. He had his love Yaya; she had him, too.

"We keep talking about Movement, but I figure

There is no way to
Move on
It's all the same journey
The only way out is
Death

Once upon a time
Before we started
This all in 2012
I was a *Vida Loca*
Loco
And now
Today
After all
The Love made
Battles fought
I am still just

A *Vida Loca*
Loco

The story began before me
The story continues
The story has no conclusion
As long as it is
Vida
And as long as it is
Loca
You know you got the good stuff

We start with one idea and
We end with the same idea

I got no wisdom
Except to grumble

Get it and
Give it
While you can
All of it

Because one day there will be
No more tomorrow
Then you will have
Nothing
Then no one will even know your name
Now is the time for rhyme
The test for the best
The lust for life is stronger than
The despair of death."

Alex looked good, healthy. Sometimes we work out together and even lace up the boxing gloves, go a few rounds.

"Hell yeah," I said, "It's New Year's twenty fourteen, and I'm gonna live for lust right now. Let's dance!" I grabbed my girl. He embraced Yaya, his *amor*. It was cold, but we had a fiery blast. The hipsters in Doc's Clock bar on Mission and 22nd Street were looking at us crazy, but fuckem.

Now, today, Valentine's, is another celebration, my 22nd birthday. We got lots to be grateful for. We're gonna kick it hard, me becoming an old man. Toasts of tequila followed by cuts of tart green limes. Next month's Alex's birthday, and, by then we'll have built even more. We'll kick it hard for him, too. That's the goal, do all the craziest, most beautiful things, and go and party afterwards and invent even more for *la gente*!

And it don't matter haters hate out there in the world, or that they don't understand us, or look down on us, or want to kill us. We got *amor*. We got Movement, *Carnalismo*. I sing to the world:

If I disgust you
Look into the
Mirror
And
Smash it

I am your
Reflection
Calling you out
On your
Bullshit

Look into my
Green eyes
Do you see
Yourself?

Are you angry at me
Because
I make you
Face
The Truth?

It is not
My fault
You don't
Like

Your own
Smile

Instead of
Bashing me
Punch
Your own self
In the
Mouth
Give yourself
A shiner
Walk around
Black and blue
Brown
Like shit

See how it feels
To be the
Best

CHAPTER TEN —
ALEX NETA MEETS THE MOMENT OF TRUTH

This world is
War
All the Time

This emptiness
Needs creation
Anything
Outside of emptiness
Is evolution

There is too much reality in

Nothing

That's the problem
I don't want

Nothing

Even though
It is the truth

I want something that is
Desire
That requires
Fiction and imagination
A good story

Like this page

It is something
That carries over beyond the air and
Wastes my time
Yet at the same time
I got something to show for it

Words

Spider symbols
Some type of web
That I follow along
To a conclusion

This is it

You judge whether it is worth it
You be the smile that fills my desire
The anger I need to shout
The danger I hunt but am too
Kind to shoot

You are the reader and
The target
But I am not in control
Because without you
I do not exist
I'm just empty
Then we start all over again

No
I finish and
This is

Something

A product
Results
A measurement
That they tell me means

Something

But that I know is

Less true than
The

Nothing

That exists
First and forever

From Cortland Street, I hike up *La Loma*. It is something. Gets me
strong, strong legs, strong *nalgas*, good breath, measurement at the top—the
trillion dollar view of the city, my city, of the Bay that pours in from the
Pacific Ocean, of the bone mountains, Mount Tamalpais, Mount Diablo—
and it is only natural, purely natural, like the handsome hawk that soars in
the sky, that I come here to meditate, to inspire myself, to give myself some
peace, to heal myself. As a Native, I've been coming here my entire life.
With heavy *carne asada* burrito in plastic bag, I carry a heavy load, thinking
of Yaya, *mi amor*, thinking of despair and regret, but not thinking because I
move; I can get to the mountain top, and it will be something, proof that once
upon a time, I did something with my life.

Bernal Heights, you bless me.

I turned 28 a little over two weeks ago on Fat Tuesday, March Fourth,
the year of *Amor*, 2014. Yeah, born on March Forth, I am a natural born
revolutionary, and that is simply what it is. We had a good time, Lil Santo,
Toro, Cartoon, Yaya, her kids. They bought me a cake and sang me *Las
Mañanitas*. Then it was the next day.

Fat Tuesday burned into
Ashes on Wednesday
The first day of suffering
Lent

The fat greasy cholesterol of
Consciousness kills

Death is the only sincerity

But before you go
Be a glutton

Enjoy *la locura*

On my birthday
On fat ass Tuesday
We had
Pura Neta
Ah huevo!
Drinking
Smoking
Eating
Insanity

The next day
We had to be burned
Incinerated
So that only
Ashes exist
Ash Wednesday

Look for me in the gray ash of obscurity
Where there exists no black or white
Answers
Only gray

Now it's finally clear
Gray can be precise and beautiful too
Gray calculates
A color unto itself

Suffering

That is also
Pura Neta
That explodes energy
Blessings

No matter what happens
You know what to look forward to:

Ashes to ashes
Dust to dust
From dust you came
To dust you shall return

Yaya and me got into a stupid argument after my birthday, and we haven't really been good ever since, for almost two weeks. We yelled, screamed, and stayed silent, which is always the worst.

It hurts to hurt the one you love and
To be hurt by the one you love

Today is Friday, March 21, 2014, about 7:00 p.m. I got to go to work at 9:00. Friday night is gonna be busy as fuck at Tip Top's nightclub, but I'm glad at least work takes my mind off of everything. I got on my black 49ers cap and my locsters shades to block the sun, which is gonna set at 7:22, which is gonna be a beautiful sight, but for now there's still a lot of light out. I'm dressed in my black security guard uniform, got my taser, too, so I can skip right to work after I meditate on this mountain. I'm wearing my new red niners jacket, cause that star Kaepernick got us all the way to the NFC Championship this year. I'm proud of my city.

It's a nice afternoon, brisk. This mountaintop helps me, but I can feel Today the mountain is strange.

I look up and see the hawk circling around, seemingly following me.

I get to the road winding around Bernal Heights, and I meet a dog, not the fluffy one that wants my burrito, but the fat white dog who will call me a spic.

I see this white man, this Snowflake, leering at women's asses; he almost breaks his neck. He doesn't give a fuck that they give him dirty looks. His unleashed dog, something like a Siberian Husky, doesn't really give a fuck either, and though it looks kind of like a wolf, it could never be a *loco* Lobo. It has the heart of a spoiled ass white dog. Man, I love dogs, have my own blue nose pit bitch and sometimes even take care of the OG Toro's golden pit bull Diamond, but this white Husky is a disrespectful dog, not asking nicely for a bite of my burrito, but thinking it is his privilege to take the whole damn thing! And his overweight owner is not caring what the fuck his dog is doing. A vicious pit bull—I love; a privileged white man's dog is

200

disrespect and danger.

"Hey, get your dog!" I call over to four-eyed fat man. His dog starts barking at me, howling, and the owner smiles, like it's a beautiful song to him, to have his wild dog attack an innocent Brown man. He doesn't even try to talk with the dog. I start quick-walking further down to some benches overlooking the Twin Peaks view, cause that's where I want to eat my burrito, but now this fucking white dog is starting to chase me. I jog over to the bench and jump on the seat.

"Get your fucking dog!" I yell directly at Snowflake. I swear that motherfucker laughs. That's when I'm like, Fuck It. This motherfucking man and his dog are an attack team, like how during the civil rights era those police officers used to sick their dogs on the Black *gente*. I pull out my taser that I happen to have on me because, like I said, I'm just gonna be going to work after my meditation and burrito. Lucky for me that I brought it—for this racist ass dog that I had no idea I would meet.

Today the mountain is strange.

"What are you doing?" Preppy Snowflake is shocked, maybe because a Mexican stands up to him and his piece of shit dog.

"I told you to get your fucking dog, man." I have my taser pointed at the dog, but it's still barking and howling at me. I don't want to shoot it, don't shoot it, am not a violent man, give the dog a chance, more than he would ever give me.

"Come here, Boy," he yells to his dog. Yep, that's right: his dog's name is actually Boy, exactly what those white racists used to call fully grown Black and Brown men. But Boy doesn't come. Damn, this white man is actually up here with his out-of-control dog that's not on a leash while he's drooling off women's asses, and now, I got to convince this dumb fucking racist how to handle this situation.

This is not the era of the 1950's Civil Rights movement.

I point the taser at him. "Get your fucking dog," I order him.

He gets on his knees and starts speaking sweetly, "Come here, Boy." The dog hesitantly trots towards him. Then white man starts yelling obscenities at me. He must realize I have only a taser, especially because of the yellow markings all over it. I don't feel the need to explain anything to him, cause I just needed that dog immediately off me.

"You fucking spic," he shouts at me. "You must think you're a bad ass."

"Huh?" I can't believe it. "You couldn't control your dog, you white punk." I holster back my security guard work taser.

He smiles. He laughs. He had waited for this

Moment

His entire life.

"Ha, ha, you're the dirty greasy wetback, not me," he snickers. "What do you have there in the bag?" He seems to try to make out the shape in my plastic bag. "Oh, it's a burrito! You fucking beaner!" He is giddy.

I laugh. "White man," I, too, had waited for

This

Moment

My entire
Life

"For you to invent an insult out of beans, you are all fucked up." I stand on the bench and preach to the sky:

"Beans are good for you
Protein makes you strong
Helps you grow
They are clean
Natural
From the ground
Brown like me

Beans are
Magic
Like
The Beans
In
Jack and the Beanstalk

White man
Don't you know it is

An honor
To be a
Bean?"

"Fuck you," Snowflake snarls. "I wish I was in Florida and had my gun."

The gall!

He has to be referring to Trayvon Martin, and how that white punk George Zimmerman got off from getting prosecuted after killing 14 year old Black Trayvon in Florida. It's just me and him and shaggy dog throughout this entire incident. I wonder if he would be this racist if other white folks were around. Four-eyed fat man then takes out his phone, but puts it away almost as quickly as he pulls it out, maybe because he knows he is to blame in this situation, his dog running around all loose and stupid, attacking me even, while he's looking at women's asses. Plus, he knows all I have is a taser.

He doesn't call the cops.

He walks away, mumbling, spitting shit, like a lunatic, worse than the homeless men I know.

I still need to eat my super *carne asada* burrito. I mean, that's the whole reason I hiked up here, to chill before a busy Friday night at work.

But I don't want to be at the same benches anymore.

Fucked up vibes.

So I stroll down and around the road about a hundred yards to the next set of benches overlooking the *corazón* of the Mission.

It is about 7:08 p.m. when I try to relax. Fuck it, I'm hungry.

What a gorgeous view, air and mountains, water and wood, buildings and bridges, the powerful hawk, and all of *La Misión*! What a beautiful fucked up world! That's why me and Lil Santo do the movement, all *amor*.

That's why my heart is breaking for Yaya.

My heart is a heavy load that is fragile.

I sink my teeth into the soft juicy burrito. It's good. It helps. Man, I want to feel good, do feel good, there's so much to be grateful for—*jalapenos y carne asada*!

Thanks
Not
Thank You
Just Thanks

To an omniscient impossibility I still believe is there beyond my eyes
To the homeless men down the block who smile at me and know my name
To my temple, my mind, my body, my spirit and soul, pain and happiness
To all of those invisible animals that roar and that only I can hear

Just Thanks

For another day, another dollar
For dancing on the streets and eating and drinking and loving and living

Just Thanks

Because the suffering is only an illusion
Because *los pinches Indios* sacrificed this land to ungrateful children
Because Heaven and Hell are the same entity, the same lie or
misunderstanding or mystery

It is all a miracle
It is all cause for
Thanks
And
Damnation

My entire life I have been in
The middle of
Thanks
And
Damnation
So on this day
I simply
Choose
Thanks

Just Thanks

And I want to stay thankful, want to stay positive, but, damn, that piece
of shit and his dog fucked up my day. Can't completely shake that shit off.

They're the new attack dog team on Bernal Heights. This is not 1960's Alabama. Their dogs are different but the same. Their words are different, but their hearts are the same. But, no, these new people can't all be bad. They can't all make-believe that Beaners is an insult. They can't be that stupid, can they?

No, they would laugh with me about this ridiculousness. I'm just a Mexican eating a burrito! Nothing, nothing at all to worry about here.

Yeah, they can't all be that fucked up. Impossible. I hear them murmuring on the road behind me. Without turning my neck around, I already know who they are. Yuppy hipsters. Tall skinny white men wearing bifocals, strolling their doggie in a baby carriage down the mountain, both the owners and doggie wearing matching knitted sweaters. I don't need to turn around to know who they are. But they just can't all be that bad. I've seen some version of them for about the past fifteen years, as this area got more and more gentrified.

Now I am the stranger.

Today both this mountain and I are strange.

Usually I would eat this whole beautiful burrito. But I don't want it all today, got my appetite spoiled. It's ok, though, because I just rewrap it in its tinfoil and save it in my bag, will eat it later, and once again the magic beans will help me.

I get up at 7:13. I throw out some punches, like Toro, shadowboxing, pretending that I am the middleweight champion of the world. I make a joke out of myself, like Cartoon would want me to do.

Beaner Boxer :)

I got tomorrow. I will patch things up with Yaya *mañana*.

But, man, I can't wait until *mañana*. I love her today. What if there is no *mañana*?

I remember Cartoon telling me about the way Lil Santo's father used to be, *Todo Bodo* Down, is what he used to say. It helps me understand the Mission of old days, mass incarceration and murder days, days of honor and insanity. It helps me understand how mama Maricela loved Big Santo and why she loves Lil Santo so much. It is my example for *amor*, that which I give to Yaya. Cartoon told us this was Santo's song:

"If I go forward
Follow me
If I hesitate

Push me
If they kill me
Avenge me
If I am a traitor
Kill me

Many try
Many die
Few succeed
In the life
We lead."

Cartoon stated the Spirit of Santo. I remember smiling because I thought it was beautiful. I still think it is, but I'm growing into my own mind, and now I see it is incomplete because

Their old street creed was wrong—
The Day of Death is a day we must
All
Celebrate
Both a victory and a defeat
A day of ending
A night of beginning

So I sing my own
Death song
Knowing
There is no escape
And why not?

This *vida loca*
This dream or
Nightmare
It is all the same

If I can sing death
Then
I can sing life, too

'Lay your head
Upon my pillow
Hold your warm and
Tender body close to mine
For the Good Times.'

I miss you, Yaya. I love you. Somehow this pure mountain helps me,
treats me right. I look down across the view, and it's my city, Frisco! The
overwhelming skyscrapers, the hoods, *La Misión*, Potrero Hill, Downtown;
the Golden Gate Bridge, all of it is mine, and I feel it. I love it, whether
it loves me back or not. Been lookin out at this view my whole twenty-
eight years of life, searching for something in it. Some impossible dream. I
command myself--

Search
Keep looking
You will find it and
When you do
Don't hoard it
Love it and
Let it kill you

It's the only way to live
It's the only way to die
Your way
Your passion
Your Love

Even if you are afraid
Even though you know
You will die
So what?
It is only
Death
A make-believe word
Your Love
Your feelings

Are greater than words

What better dream
Is there but to
Love and to
Be killed
By what
You Love?

San Francisco

I smile at the courage of this place, my city, my mountain, my hawk, my bones, and I know I gotta just keep moving.

"What's up with the Movement, Homes?!" I say it with a snarl and laugh out loud cause that's the way me and Lil Santo greet each other, and from that moment forward, it's always on.

This is
La Movida
The Movement
So I walk

Now that I have been to the

Mountain top

There is only
Down

I mosey down the mountain, turn the bend, see a cop car without flashing lights, without sirens blaring, driving up smoothly, in a calculated fashion, towards me. Some shit must have happened around here, but I'm glad it aint me. They must be looking for some criminal. That can't be me, cause I've never even been arrested in my entire life. Shit,

I'm a security guard.

It is 7:18 p.m. Two white cops jump out of their patrol car, aim their pistols at me and

Start
Shooting

Two more cops come
A white one and a
Chinese one

They all unload
Pulling their triggers
Again and again
Reloading their magazines
59 bullets
14 hits

I see myself. I am beyond who I am. I have turned into something else.
Today it is strange that the mountain and I are now one.
No, I am no longer here.
I am flying like the hawk, who has witnessed everything, but I am not
my noble Brother hawk who soars and stays in this world. I hear him, but
I also hear something else, the wind whooshing, a song—something like a
theme song, an anthem with lots of cow bell clanging, cymbals crashing,
trumpets blowing.
I sail with my Brother hawk in all his majesty and listen to the music
of the wind, the lyrics of Nature: "Blow the trumpet; sound the alarm on My
holy mountain! Let all who dwell in the land tremble, for the Day is coming;
in fact, it is at hand."
I wear a cape, just like my comic book heroes. Just like Superman, but I
knew early on in my life I could never be Superman with peach skin and blue
eyes.
Made by magic beans, I am beyond Superman.
How can I see myself down there and yet be flying at the same time?
I have flown to my destiny. I have reached the name that blessed me in
this life, the word that is the purpose of everything, the only super power on
planet earth and in the heavens:

Neta:
Truth
Imagination

The same thing

 I am beyond myself and also inside of my dreams as a child.

I am

SUPERHOMES

No
Bright
American dreamers
I'm not talking about
McMansions
With white-picket
French fry fences

"Look!
Up, up
In the sky!"

It's not a bird or
A plane or
Sherlock HOLMES

It's

SUPERHOMES,

Homes
Short and Sweet
For Homeboy
But not your average *loco*

A star
A savior
Who can stand tall and
Stouthearted
Facing off against

Four armed cops
59 bullets they fire
And shit their pants
Against me
Because I am

SUPERHOMES

Shot at 59 times
Shot 14 points in my
Head
Face
Lung, leg
Spine, shoulders
Wrist
Hand
Forearm

I fly to the floor because I am

SUPERHOMES

And the police keep firing
And I shake that shit off
And keep maddogging them
Through my locsters
With my X-ray eyes
Examining their souls
Of fear and stupidity

They will confess this in court:

"I was scared for my life."

But

I

SUPERHOMES

I

(If we are to believe their
Official reports)

I was *mas chingón*
Badder than Scarface
Never surrendering
All the fucking way, *ese*!

Now I know you all
Aint never had too many heroes
Except for the
Dope-dealers and
Hustlers and
Penitentiary gangsters
But I will try to deserve that honor as

SUPERHOMES

A.K.A. mild mannered
Alex Neta
In my
Once upon a time
Human disguise

I will be your *varrio* hero

"Look!
Up, up
In the sky"

I still fly high

Not Forward but
Upward

For Truth
Justice and
The American Way

CHAPTER ELEVEN — THE REVOLT OF THE ROOTS

Revolution belongs to eternity
Revolution was yesterday
Revolution is right now
Revolution will be *mañana*

Revolution and evolution are
The same thing:
One cannot exist without the other

The roots are the reason all flowers bloom

On Friday, March 21, 2014, Alex Neta got whacked by the cops for eating a burrito in a gentrified neighborhood, Bernal Heights, San Fran, *Califas*, aka, *Aztlan*. Fifty nine gunshots cracked open the heavens, his spirit rose off the ground, and the insane angels zoomed out of the sky to start some good shit.

His blood was the roots
We are the flowers

Two years later, on Tuesday, May 3, 2016, over 1,000 flowers bloomed brightly, splashing iridescent colors on Frisco's City Hall and on its Board of Supervisors' Chambers, during their formal monthly meeting. Underneath all that carved Victorian beauty and etched artisan work, the Board attempted excuses, performed mediocre rants of rhetoric:

"We can do nothing to help you."

Face to face with the Board, the *locos* and *locas* stood strong, all of them, Brown, Black, White, Asian, Gay, Straight, Muslims, Jews, Gentiles, Young and Old, Educated, Street Folks, Roots, including me (Lil Santo), and Cartoon, Toro, Maricela, and even Santo the Spirit, my pops. We had the Board exactly where we wanted them.

"Fire Chief Sure! Fire Chief Sure! Fire Chief Sure!" in unison, in harmony, in that unmistakable music of the masses' madness and genius.

The Board was scared of us, scared of their own shadows, the *gente* from underground. They thought we were crazy, and they were right.

Less than a month later, the chief of police of one of the most powerful cities on planet earth got booted cause we booted him. Even with their trillion dollars against us, their entire propaganda machine, and all their laws and lies, we changed shit. We fired the chief and all the scared politicians started trying to come over to our side. We sparked mass movement, *amor* art, lowrider revolution. Chief Sure didn't resign. It wasn't no request by the mayor. It wasn't no good old fashioned civil rights movement.

The Revolt of the Roots:

*Loca*s *y Locos*
Homeboys and Homegirls
Me (Lil Santo)
Cartoon
Mama Maricela
El Toro
Lobo locked up
Santo the Spirit
La Misión
San Francisco

On the
Frontline
Taking over shit
Stirring the pot
Creating concoctions of craziness and
Putting it all into action

That is what changed history
A history that will never be known unless
Natural Roots write it out
Put their lives on the line and
Push progress

Amor for Alex Neta

GLOSSARY

Amerigo Vespucci: 15th century Italian explorer who discovered nothing, but who did realize that "America" was not China or any continent previously known. America, therefore, is named after the first person who told the Europeans that they were wrong and did not even know where they were or who they are.

Amor: Love. Lots of Love. All *Amor*. Romantic Love. Family Love. Brotherly Love. Sisterly Love. Love for animals. Love for human beings. Christian Love. Buddhist Love. Love transcending human understanding or logic. Empathy. Mindfulness. Forgiveness. Redemption. All *Amor*.

Aztlán: The mythical homeland of the Aztecs, the ancient Mesoamerican civilization also known as the Mexica.

Balmy Alley: Located in the Mission District in San Francisco. The block long alley holds the most concentrated collection of murals in the city. Since the mid-80's, artists have expressed outrage over human rights and political abuses in their local community and beyond. Many of the murals highlight issues such as gentrification and police brutality.

Barrio Bushido: *Barrio*: Neighborhood. *Bushido*: The code of the Samurai warrior. *Barrio Bushido* is about the unwritten, illogical code of the streets. The code to purposely choose the most destructive and painful manner in any given situation. This was the code of honor of the streets in the 1980's and 1990's. It was a code that accepted death and mass incarceration and attempted to overcome inequalities and injustice with its own spirit for street warriors. Cartoon mentions that during his educational and spiritual odyssey he wrote a book called *Barrio Bushido*.

Beaner: A derogatory term for a person of Latino/a descent. Alex Neta notes that the term should actually be viewed as a compliment, as beans provide protein and power to people.

Bernal Heights: The highest peak in San Francisco's 94110 region, which includes the Mission and Bernal Heights neighborhoods. Prior to the 2000's, it was known as a lover's lane/inspiration point for locals. Young people would party hard up on the mountain. Boxers and other athletes would use the mountain for training purposes.

Brain Bushido: A mindful strategic code of honor rooted in our natural minds. According to Lobo, *Barrio Bushido* must be abandoned for a *Brain Bushido* in order to overcome systemic oppression and technological manipulation that is plaguing the community.

Capitalism: A system that purports to be based on an economic laissez-faire free market meritocracy, but that has always been and still is subsidized by governments for the benefit of elite corporations and at the expense of working class people. According to Lobo, we are moving into an era when capitalism is becoming obsolete, as actual physical capital is not even necessary anymore; technology's "data-ism" Cloud is not even reliant on any physical capital.

Carnales: Brothers of the flesh. Brothers of the spirit.

Carnaval in La Mision: Since 1979 in San Francisco, one of the biggest and most diverse carnival parades in the entire world. Associated with Mardi Gras, Fat Tuesday, which is the celebration before Ash Wednesday, which begins the Catholic season of suffering and sacrifice: Lent.

Cholo/a: A term that originated as an insult meaning a mutt dog, but which has come to identify a Latino/a American gangster *vida loca loco/a* full of pride and hutzpah, a person, perhaps unable to articulate their oppression, but who is conscious of it and refuses to accept it.

Feria: money, cash, fare.

Gang injunctions: A restraining order against a gang of people of color. In California no gang injunction has ever targeted a white gang. The order uses the power of the court to declare the gang's public behavior a nuisance and uses the police to keep public streets clear of these groups of color, while allowing other groups to flourish, especially young white hipster groups. Many opponents of gang injunctions argued that they were a tool not to fight crime, but to further gentrification by harassing longtime residents and pressuring them to leave their homes, to be replaced by wealthier and generally whiter newcomers. Toro poses that "It's all meant to be an intimidation, and like Maricela said, a military occupation. It aint no coincidence that the gang injunctions are targeted here in *La Misión*. Man, that shit is just an excuse to erase us and keep our brown skin out of sight so that the newbies aint gotta feel threatened. Convinced even lots of our own people that we're the bad guys when we're really just patsies of the system."

Gold mountain: San Fran Frisco San Francisco, the city of presumed overflowing wealth and opportunity. Associated with the myth of SF 49ers gold.

Grunt: First to fight frontline Marine, a rifleman, machine-gunner, mortar man, or anti-tank assault man.

Hipster: A white (usually) middle or upper-economic class person promoting an overly trendy fashion, style, and consumerist mindset who believes they are hip and conscious yet are ignorant about oppression and injustice.

Indio: In Latin America one of the worst insults one can use against a person of Indigenous descent, akin to the "N" word in the U.S. The insult attributes stereotypes of stupidity and savageness to those of Indigenous descent.

Ira Hayes: A Pima Native American Marine who helped raise the United States flag on Mount Suribachi during the infamous battle of Iwo Jima. The photo of the flag-raising became one of the most iconic images of the 20th century. After returning from World War II, Hayes suffered from Post-Traumatic Stress Disorder and began drinking heavily. In 1955 he was found frozen to death on an Arizona Indian reservation.

La Pinta: The penitentiary, the rite of passage for many young men of color, especially during the mass incarceration era that began in the 1980's.

La Segunda: Second-hand thrift stores like the Salvation Army.

Lechuga: Money, green lettuce.

Maricela: A female name associated with the Roman and Greek god of war.

Mass incarceration: Beginning in the early 1980's, a punitive system justified by "law and order" to incarcerate, en masse, criminals for extended periods of time, especially for drug related crimes. Most people mass incarcerated are people of color.

Maton: Angel dust, literally killer, colloquially known as dust, KJ (killer joint), a raw one. Known for its hallucinogenic effects. The drug of choice for *vida loca* gang-members of the 80's, as it erased the feeling of existence for a brief period (e.g. an hour) and then would lead to a rush of adrenaline, hyper-consciousness, and physical activity.

Militarization of police: Rooted in a 1981 enactment entitled the Military Cooperation with Law Enforcement Act, which allowed the U.S. military to give law enforcement agencies access to its military bases, training, and its military equipment. The legislation was promoted during the Presidency of Ronald Reagan in the context of the War on Drugs and is considered a part of a general trend towards the militarization of police.

Movida Movement: Conscious uprising of the people.

Nieto, Alex: March 4, 1986 to March 21, 2018.

Nuestra Señora de Dolores: Our Lady of Sorrows, Jesus Christ's mother, Mary Maria, who is usually depicted with seven swords piercing her sorrowful heart that is bleeding and suffering for her murdered son.

One antidote: Death, murder.

Paranoia: For people of color, the feeling that America and white society is against you, but that if you articulate this, you will be deemed deviant, clinically insane—because most Americans believe that America is the land of freedom and equal opportunity. According to Toro, paranoia is both a curse and a strength, for even though a crazy homeboy is always unsure about every little movement and sound, a crazy homeboy also knows his insanity will never abandon him; therefore, he stays ready for constant battle.

¡Presente!: Present, in the moment, a call and response slogan usually shouted to commemorate the dead, to ask a specific dead person to be there with the group in that present at moment. Stated emphatically with the belief that person's dead spirit will help them in their struggle and celebration. E.g. Call: "¡Alex Nieto!" Response: "*¡Presente!*"

Pura Neta: Spanish street slang for pure truth. Fiction and reality combined, a bridge between imagination and truth, which is the same thing, for truth was once simply imagination, and imagination is necessary for the evolution of truth.

Quilmas: San Quentin a famous California prison known for spawning super gangs.

REDRUM: Murder.

San Francisco: Saint Francis, a saint who abandoned his entire wealth to dedicate himself to peace, love, chastity, and the root principles of Christianity; who had the ability to communicate with animals and suffered from the stigmata. San Francisco, California takes its namesake from him and purports itself to be the most progressive place on planet earth, despite its hedonism, racism, and economic and educational inequality.

Sick with it: The best, a highly acclaimed status and show of respect, someone who is proving the *vida loca* philosophy. In *Barrio Bushido*, Santo explains this consciousness: "If we are sick," Santo said, "we got a lot of responsibility with that title. It means we live the life, and we die. That's it. It means we don't give a fuck. It means we know we don't give a fuck."

Soul Oldies: The standard music of *vida loca locos* y *locas*. African-American rare soul sounds of the 60's and 70's, a music genre that spoke intimately to *gente* who were and are experiencing love and pain.

Spider Symbols: Letters of the alphabet, an inexact attempt at reality. Language is the basis for human understanding, but no words, written or verbal, can ever equal the actual thing, as all words are simply symbols attempting to explain reality. Words, these words, are actually nothing more than lines and curves on a page, yet human beings believe them because the educational institutions condition them to believe that words and language equal truth.

Spirit Matters Most: The idea that words, language, policies, education, etc. are not as important or substantive as the indescribable inarticulable feeling within humans that knows something beyond reality. This spirit, some believe, is the guiding force for all substance.

Technology: A systemized technique of getting things "efficiently" accomplished. Many people believe that efficiency through algorithms is the ultimate reality and goal of human beings' civilization. Educational institutions, for example, promote that efficient hard work is an egalitarian virtue.

Tecun Uman: Early 16th century K'iche' Mayan warrior who fought against and was killed by Spain's Pedro de Alvarado.

The Grand Capitalist: Inspired by Fyodor Dostoevsky's The Grand Inquisitor from The Brothers Karamazov. The Grand Capitalist offers outstanding logical human arguments regarding capitalism's benefits, such as the cure for starvation and disease, the glory of education and intelligence, long life, material wealth, and the efficiency of technology. He argues Christianity is stupid and selfish because Jesus' ideal can never be realized by most simplistic and greedy human beings, so the ideal merely causes them to waste their life and needlessly suffer. In rebuttal to these excellent arguments, Jesus Christ kisses The Grand Capitalist who tortures him. Love is not necessarily a winning argument, but it is Jesus' only response to such irrefutable human logic.

The Pachuco Cross: The *Pachuco* cross is an embedded tradition of the *loco* lifestyle, going as far back as the 1940's Zoot Suit era. It was usually tattooed directly on the hand, between the thumb and index finger—during an era when tattoos were uncommon, especially tattoos that were noticeable in public. The tattooed person represents a *vato loco* who loves to party, dance, fight, love, and howl. Although he knows he is a sinner, he is also someone who pays reverence to religion: the sacrifice, pain, and love of Christ's crucifixion and metaphysical power.

"This is Take Off": Written on Santo's tombstone and viewed by Cartoon as both stupid and genius. Stupid because Santo is dead, which in logical existential terms is the opposite of a Take Off, for example, by a plane. Genius because death is the only true Take Off, as it is the only plane that can rocket past the universe.

Trayvon Martin: Fourteen year old African American youth killed by George Zimmerman in 2013. Zimmerman was absolved from any culpability even though he was the initial aggressor and was armed. Florida's "Stand

Your Ground" law provided legal justification for what many believe was cold-blooded murder.

Tupac Inca Yupanqui: Tenth Sapa Inca emperor of the Inca Empire.

Vatos Locos: Crazy guys, *cholos* dedicated to *vida loca*.

Vendidos: Traitors, sell-outs.

Vida Loca: Crazy life, the *cholo/a* philosophy that existence is absurd and insane, including nature, education, and human-constructed rationales. It is not a nihilistic philosophy; on the contrary it is life affirming in that it provides an understanding and accepting of chaos. The adherent embraces destruction and, because of this, treasures the impromptu moment.

Vincent 'The Chin' Gigante: Former boss of the Genovese Crime Family. For thirty years he feigned insanity in public so that he could clandestinely continue to run his criminal organization without him being arrested or prosecuted.

White flight: The myth that after World War II whites left the inner cities because they did not want to live amongst people of color. In The Color of Law, Richard Rothstein argues that it was not white flight at all, but an invitation by the federal government for whites only to purchase homes in newly invented suburbs that promoted the façade of universal golden era happiness and prosperity.

Wilas: Secret messages, kites, sent amongst prison inmates in order to conduct prison business.

WOKE: Conscious.

ACKNOWLEDGMENTS

I thank perfect strangers for that is who you are and who I am, even to myself. We have been on a journey together, and now we come to the end, or perhaps, simply the beginning. I thank you for engaging me in your minds, your most intimate space, you, who have never heard my voice, but who know me in all of my nakedness on the page. Without you my words are meaningless.

We are perfect strangers.

Familia.

To God, that which is both blasphemous and holy, for some say we are not even worthy enough to write out the letters, which are a graven image; while others say God is the omnipotent power of the universe that deserves the highest praise: Hallelujah!

I thank the courage and the cowardice. Sometimes one turns out to be the other, and I am grateful for that, too: the confusion.

I thank the writers I stole from, for that is what reading and writing are all about—stealing and sharing. Dostoevsky, Francísco Ximénez, Garcia-Marquez, Camus, Shakur, Hong-Kingston, Pessoa, Cohen, Loynaz, Ellul, Bukowski, Kafka, Freire, Argueta, Alexander, X, Tsunetomo, Panero, Wright, *y más!*

My Sisters and Brothers, Homeboys and Homegirls, lost souls who guide me through this maze of life. For mercy, the savior that connects our humanity together. My family that teaches me the meaning of love: Tanya. Benny. Margaritas :) For Monica, Xiomara and Daniel Zarazua, Pochino Press, who had the faith to transform this book into *Pura Neta*. For Tom Farber, a wise man. Maxine Hong Kingston, *un alma de amor*. For the schools, especially the school of hard knocks. My teachers and inspirations. My students who teach me. The Marine Corps. All of my supporters who championed my first novel, *Barrio Bushido*. Thanks to those frontline warriors who have fought with me on the streets and in the trenches. *Amor* for Alex Nieto. It was through your grassroots spirit that this latest book is now possible. Shawna Yang Ryan. Tony Robles. Alejandro Murguia. Luis Javier Rodriguez. OG Rev. Harry Williams. Karl Marlantes. Ricardo Tavarez. Marco Macaroni Lowride Guardado. Roberto Hernandez. Father Richard Smith. My Muse: *La Loma*.

And finally to Alejandro "Alex" Nieto, who wrote on November 10, 2010, "Ur story struck a deep chord in my being. If you need any future work with any further books or publications, let me know…I know your book will serve to awaken young homies in *el barrio*." RIP

APPENDIX

CHAPTER ONE: FINDING BALANCE
Carnales, the inspiration for Lobo, Santo, Toro, 1991

CHAPTER TWO: EL SANTO, THE SPIRIT
SFM N Jeff RIP, *La Pinta*: California Department of Corrections,
Susanville, circa 1989.

CHAPTER THREE: CARTOON
A Cartoon Surrounded by *El Diablo* and Death.

CHAPTER FOUR: MAMA MARICELA
Mama Maricela's SHERO, Frida Kahlo adorned with Aztec imagery.
Created by Oscar Aguilar, 2020.

CHAPTER FIVE: EL TORO
Lance Corporal Benjamin Bac Sierra, 0331, Bravo Company, First Battalion Fifth Marines, Task Force Ripper Rumbling into Kuwait, Gulf War, 1991.

CHAPTER SIX: CARTOON VISITS LOBO AT SAN QUENTIN PINTA
Para La Misión, the purpose of Lobo and Cartoon's plan. Mural by Mel Waters and Hyde, 19th and Mission, San Fran Frisco.

CHAPTER SEVEN: THE MISSION OF DOLORES

La Más Firme Nuestra Señora de Dolores, Our Lady of Sorrows, Jesus Christ's mother, Maria, who is usually depicted with seven swords piercing her sorrowful heart. Stained glass art at *La Misión de San Francisco de Asis*, 16th and Dolores, San Fran Frisco.

CHAPTER EIGHT: THE GRAND CAPITALIST

Trillion dollar skyline view at Mission Dolores *Parque*, former cemetery, San Fran Frisco.

CHAPTER NINE: LIL SANTO
Los Santitos más locos, Benny y Margarita, 2011.

CHAPTER TEN: ALEX NETA MEETS THE MOMENT OF TRUTH
Alex Nieto's Blessing, 2010.

Greetings Ben,
I just arrived in Tokyo last night. I got to talk to Marcos before i left. I will seek to learn what a samurai and bushido are all about. I will seek to find the heart of a samurai fighting spirit. You readings from your book have deeply touched my heat. I know you your book will serve to awaken young homies in el barrio. I hope everything is well and look forward to seeing you in the near future.

Sayonara-Arigato
Sincerely
Alejandro Nieto , Alex

11/13/10, 6:52 PM

CHAPTER ELEVEN: THE REVOLT OF THE ROOTS
May Day Action Inside of SF City Hall, 2015.

About Benjamin Bac Sierra

Benjamin Bac Sierra was raised by a widowed mother and the streets of San
Francisco's Mission District. After serving as a grunt in the Marine Corps,
where he participated in front-line combat during the first Gulf War, Ben
completed his B.A. in English at U.C. Berkeley, earned a teaching credential
and a Master's in Creative Writing from San Francisco State University, and
merited a Juris Doctor degree from the University of California, Hastings
College of the Law. Currently, he is a professor at City College of San
Francisco and a community innovator and keynote speaker throughout the
Bay Area. Ben's essays and stories have been published in newspapers
and literary magazines, including World Literature Today, where he was
featured as a prominent emerging author. His first novel *Barrio Bushido* was
presented a Best of the Bay Award and an International Latino Book Award.
In 2016, U.C. Hastings College of the Law La Raza Students Association
honored him as a Distinguished Alumni of the Year for his community
leadership and legal analysis of police killings.

Made in the USA
Monee, IL
04 October 2020